by ARGO BROTHERS

2020 - 2021

3ʳᵈ GRADE
COMMON CORE
ELA

ENGLISH
LANGUAGE
ARTS

DAILY PRACTICE BOOK

ARGOPREP.COM

FREE ONLINE SYSTEM WITH VIDEO EXPLANATIONS

ArgoPrep is one of the leading providers of supplemental educational products and services. We offer affordable and effective test prep solutions to educators, parents and students. Learning should be fun and easy! For that reason, most of our workbooks come with detailed video answer explanations taught by one of our fabulous instructors.

Our goal is to make your life easier, so let us know how we can help you by e-mailing us at:
info@argoprep.com.

ISBN: 9781951048129
Published by Argo Brothers, Inc.

Aknowlegments:
Icons made by Freepik, Creaticca Creative Agency, Pixel perfect , Pixel Buddha, Smashicons, Twitter , Good Ware, Smalllikeart, Nikita Golubev, monkik, DinosoftLabs, Icon Pond from www.flaticon.com

- ArgoPrep is a recipient of the prestigious **Mom's Choice Award**.
- ArgoPrep also received the 2019 **Seal of Approval** from Homeschool.com for our award-winning workbooks.
- ArgoPrep was awarded the 2019 **National Parenting Products Award**, **Gold Medal Parent's Choice Award** and a **Brain Child Award**

Want an amazing offer from ArgoPrep?

7 DAY ACCESS

to our online premium content at **www.argoprep.com**

Online premium content includes practice quizzes and drills with video explanations and an automatic grading system.

Chat with us live at **www.argoprep.com** for this exclusive offer.

ARGO BROTHERS

OTHER BOOKS BY ARGOPREP

Here are some other test prep workbooks by ArgoPrep you may be interested in. All of our workbooks come equipped with detailed video explanations to make your learning experience a breeze! Visit us at **www.argoprep.com**

COMMON CORE MATH SERIES

 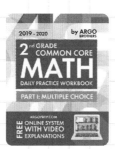  

  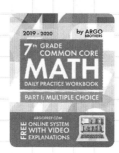 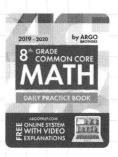

COMMON CORE ELA SERIES

INTRODUCING MATH!

Introducing Math! by ArgoPrep is an award-winning series created by certified teachers to provide students with high-quality practice problems. Our workbooks include topic overviews with instruction, practice questions, answer explanations along with digital access to video explanations. Practice in confidence - with ArgoPrep!

   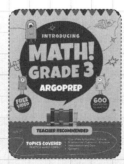 

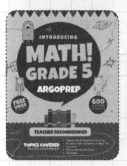   

YOGA MINDFULNESS FOR KIDS

HIGHER LEVEL EXAMS

KIDS SUMMER ACADEMY SERIES

ArgoPrep's **Kids Summer Academy** series helps prevent summer learning loss and gets students ready for their new school year by reinforcing core foundations in math, english and science. Our workbooks also introduce new concepts so students can get a head start and be on top of their game for the new school year!

Meet the ArgoPrep heroes.

Are you ready to go on an incredible adventure and complete your journey with them to become a **SUPER** student?

WATER FIRE

MYSTICAL NINJA

GREEN POISON

FIRESTORM WARRIOR

RAPID NINJA

CAPTAIN ARGO

THUNDER WARRIOR

ADRASTOS THE SUPER WARRIOR

Our **Kids Summer Academy** series by **ArgoPrep** is designed to keep students engaged with fun graphics and activities. Our curriculum is aligned with state standards to help your child prepare for their new school year.

TABLE OF
CONTENTS

HOW TO USE
THE BOOK

This workbook is designed to give lots of practice with the English Common Core State Standards (CCSS). By practicing and mastering this entire workbook, your child will become very familiar and comfortable with the ELA state exam. If you are a teacher using this workbook for your student's, you will notice each question is labeled with the specific standard so you can easily assign your students problems in the workbook. This workbook takes the CCSS and divides them up among 20 weeks. By working on these problems on a daily basis, students will be able to (1) find any deficiencies in their understanding and/or practice of english and (2) have small successes each day that will build proficiency and confidence in their abilities.

You can find detailed video explanations to each problem in the book by visiting:
www.argoprep.com/k8

We strongly recommend watching the videos as it will reinforce the fundamental concepts.

HOW TO WATCH
VIDEO EXPLANATIONS
IT IS ABSOLUTELY FREE

Download our app:
ArgoPrep Video Explanations
to access videos on any mobile device or tablet.

OR

Step 1 - Visit our website at: www.argoprep.com/k8
Step 2 - Click on "JOIN FOR FREE" button located on the top right corner.
Step 3 - Choose the grade level workbook you have.
Step 4 - Sign up as a Learner, Parent or a Teacher.
Step 5 - Register using your email or social networks.
Step 6 - From your dashboard cick on "FREE WORKBOOKS EXPLANATION" on the left and choose the workbook you have.

Let's Begin! :)

WEEK 1

VIDEO
EXPLANATIONS

Find detailed video explanations to each problem on:
ArgoPrep.com or Download our app: **ArgoPrep Video Explanations**

Excerpt from **My Father's Dragon**
By: Ruth Stiles Gannett

One cold rainy day when my father was a little boy, he met an old alley cat on his street. The cat was very drippy and uncomfortable so my father said, "Wouldn't you like to come home with me?"

This surprised the cat — she had never before met anyone who cared about old alley cats — but she said, "I'd be very much obliged if I could sit by a warm furnace, and perhaps have a saucer of milk."

"We have a very nice furnace to sit by," said my father, "and I'm sure my mother has an extra saucer of milk."

My father and the cat became good friends but my father's mother was very upset about the cat. She hated cats, particularly ugly old alley cats. "Elmer Elevator," she said to my father, "if you think I'm going to give that cat a saucer of milk, you're very wrong. Once you start feeding stray alley cats you might as well expect to feed every stray in town, and I am not going to do it!"

This made my father very sad, and he apologized to the cat because his mother had been so rude. He told the cat to stay anyway, and that somehow he would bring her a saucer of milk each day. My father fed the cat for three weeks, but one day his mother found the cat's saucer in the cellar and she was extremely angry. She whipped my father and threw the cat out the door, but later on my father sneaked out and found the cat. Together they went for a walk in the park and tried to think of nice things to talk about. My father said, "When I grow up I'm going to have an airplane. Wouldn't it be wonderful to fly just anywhere you might think of!"

"Would you like to fly very, very much?" asked the cat.

"I certainly would. I'd do anything if I could fly."

"Well," said the cat, "If you'd really like to fly that much, I think I know of a sort of a way you might get to fly while you're still a little boy."

"You mean you know where I could get an airplane?"

"Well, not exactly an airplane, but something even better. As you can see, I'm an old cat now, but in my younger days I was quite a traveler. My traveling days are over but last spring I took just one more trip and sailed to the Island of Tangerina, stopping at the port of Cranberry. Well, it just so happened that I missed the boat, and while waiting for the next I thought I'd look around a bit. I was particularly interested in a place called Wild Island, which we had passed on our way to Tangerina. Wild Island and Tangerina are joined together by a long string of rocks, but people never go to Wild Island because it's mostly jungle and inhabited by very wild animals. So, I decided to go across the rocks and explore it for myself. It certainly is an interesting place, but I saw something there that made me want to weep."

Authors use dialogue, the words spoken by a character, to help the reader understand the events of a story. Dialogue can also help you understand what a character's personality is like.

Exercises

1. Who did the father meet when he was a little boy?

   (A.) a cat
   B. a dog
   C. a peddler
   D. a witch

4. Which word is a synonym for the word *obliged* in the text?

   A. helped
   B. sorry
   (C.) grateful
   D. angry

2. What is another word for furnace?

   A. generator
   B. air conditioner
   C. stove
   (D.) heater

5. What does the father hope to have when he grows up?

   A. a mansion
   (B.) an airplane
   C. a boat
   D. a big family

3. What can the cat do?

   (A.) talk
   B. sing
   C. read
   D. drive

6. What does the cat say happened to her?

   A. She missed her flight.
   (B.) She missed the boat.
   C. She took the wrong train.
   D. Her car had a flat tire.

Excerpt from **The Little Red House**

Very few grown-up people understand houses. Only children understand them properly, and, if I understand them just a little, it is because I knew Sym. Sym and his wife, Emily Ann, lived in the Little Red House. It was built on a rather big mountain, and there were no other houses near it. At one time, long ago, the mountain had been covered all over with a great forest; but men had cut the trees down, all but one big Blue-gum, which grew near the Little Red House. The Blue-gum and the Little Red House were great friends, and often had long talks together. The Blue-gum was a very old tree — over a hundred years old — and he was proud of it, and often used to tell of the time, long ago...

Once upon a time I put a verse about the mountain and the Little Red House into a book of rhymes, which I wrote for grown ups. I don't think they thought much about it. Very likely they said, "Oh, it's just a house on a hill," and then forgot it, because they were too busy about other things.

This is the rhyme:

A great mother mountain, and kindly is she,

Who nurses young rivers and sends them to sea.

And, nestled high up on her sheltering lap,

Is a little red house, with a little straw cap

That bears a blue feather of smoke, curling high,

And a bunch of red roses cocked over one eye.

I have tried here to draw the Little Red House for you as well as I can; and it isn't my fault if it happens to look just a little like somebody's face. I can't help it, can I? if the stones of the door-step look something like teeth, or if the climbing roses make the windows look like a funny pair of spectacles. And if Emily Ann will hang bib fluffy bobs on the window blinds for tassels, and if they swing about in the breeze like moving eyes, well, I am not to blame, am I? It just happens. The only thing I am sorry for is that I couldn't get the big Blue-gum into the picture. Of course, I could have drawn it quite easily, but it was too big.

Sym and Emily Ann were fond of the Little Red House, and you may be sure the Little Red House was fond of them — he was their home. The only thing that bothered him was that they were sometimes away from home, and then he was miserable, like all empty houses.

Now, Sym was a tinker — a travelling tinker. He would do a little gardening and farming at home for a while, and then go off about the country for a few days, mending people's pots and pans and kettles. Usually Sym left Emily Ann at home to keep the Little Red House company, but now and then Emily Ann went with Sym for a trip, and then the Little Red House was very sad indeed.

One morning, just as the sun was peeping over the edge of the world, the big Blue-gum woke up and stretched his limbs and waited for the Little Red House to say "Good morning." The Blue-gum always waited for the greeting because he was the older, and he liked to have proper respect shown to him by young folk, but the Little Red House didn't say a word.

It can be a great idea to make write down the name of each character in a story, along with notes about what he or she has done or said that has been important. This can help you to make sense of the plot.

The big Blue-gum waited and waited; but the Little Red House wouldn't speak.

After a while the Blue-gum said rather crossly, "You seem to be out of sorts this morning."

But the Little Red House wouldn't say a word.

"You certainly do seem as if you had a pain somewhere," said the Blue-gum. "And you look funny. You ought to see yourself!"

"Indeed?" snapped the Little Red House, raising his eyebrows just as a puff of wind went by. "I can't always be playing the fool, like some people."

"I've lived on this mountain, tree and sapling, for over a hundred years," replied the big Blue-gum very severely, "and never before have I been treated with such disrespect. When trees become houses they seem to lose their manners."

"Forgive me," cried the Little Red House. "I didn't mean to be rude. I was just listening. There are things going on inside me that I don't like."

"I hope they aren't ill-treating you," said the Blue-gum.

"They are going to leave me!" sighed the Little Red House.

"And they are laughing quite happily, as if they were glad about it. There's a nice thing for you! — Going to leave me, and laughing about it!"

"But perhaps you are wrong," said the big Blue-gum, who was not so hard-hearted as he seemed.

"I always know," moaned the Little Red House. "I can't be mistaken. Sym was singing his Tinker's song this morning long before the sun was up. And then I heard him tell Emily Ann not to forget her umbrella. That means that she is going; and the little dog is going, and I shall be all alone."

Exercises

1. Where is the Little Red House?

   A. in the desert
   B. on a mountain
   C. by the sea
   D. in the forest

   CCSS.ELA-LITERACY.RL.3.1

4. Why does the Little Red House become upset?

   A. He will be alone soon.
   B. He is moving to another place.
   C. He has become damaged.
   D. He needs to be cleaned.

   CCSS.ELA-LITERACY.RL.3.1

2. What is the Blue-gum in the story?

   A. an old tree
   B. a new plant
   C. a small store
   D. a home style diner

   CCSS.ELA-LITERACY.RL.3.1

5. Which of the following is a synonym for the word *crossly* in the story?

   A. excitedly
   B. bitterly
   C. quickly
   D. lazily

   CCSS.ELA-LITERACY.RL.3.4

3. What can the Little Red House do?

   A. relocate
   B. talk
   C. disassemble itself
   D. eat

   CCSS.ELA-LITERACY.RL.3.1

6. What does Sym tell Emily Ann to bring with her?

   A. a book
   B. her dog
   C. her umbrella
   D. her purse

   CCSS.ELA-LITERACY.RL.3.1

Notes

Find detailed video explanations to each problem on:
ArgoPrep.com or Download our app: ArgoPrep Video Explanations

Excerpt from **The Boy Who Rode into the Sunset**

Once upon a time — it was not so very long ago, either — a little boy, named Neville, lived with his people in a house, which was almost in the country. That is to say, it was just at the edge of the city; and at the back of the house was a rather large hill, which was quite bald.

Neville, who was fond of playing by himself, would often wander to the top of the bald hill; and if he stood right on top of it and looked one way, toward the East, he could see right over the city, with all its tall buildings and domes and spires and smoking chimneys. But looking the other way, to the West, he could see for miles over the beautiful country, with its green fields and orchards and white roads and little farmhouses.

One evening Neville was playing alone on the top of the hill when he noticed that one of the very finest sunsets he had ever seen was just coming on. The sky in the West, away over the broad country lands, was filled with little clouds of all sorts and shapes, and they were just beginning to take on the most wonderful colors.

Neville had often before amused himself with watching clouds and the strange shapes into which they changed themselves — sometimes like great mountain ranges, sometimes like sea-waves, and very often like elephants and lions and seals and all manner of interesting things of that sort. But never before had he been able to make out so many animal shapes in the clouds. The sky was almost as good as a Zoo. There were kangaroos and elephants and a hen with chickens and wallabies and rabbits and a funny man with large ears and all sorts of other peculiar shapes.

The sun was sinking behind a distant range of hills, where a golden light shone out as if through a gateway. It was so much like a great golden gateway that Neville fell to wondering what might be found on the other side of it.

Suddenly, right in the middle of all the colored clouds, he saw one little cloud which was perfectly white, and, as he watched it, he noticed that it seemed to be shaped like a small horse. A very small horse it seemed at that distance; but, as Neville gazed, it grew bigger and bigger, just as if it were coming toward him very fast, and he was almost certain he could see its legs moving.

That startled him a little, and so he rubbed his eyes to make sure that they were not playing him tricks.

When he looked again he was more startled than ever; for the little white cloud was no longer a cloud, but a little white horse in real earnest. Besides, it had just left the sky and was galloping down the mountain range which he could see away in the West.

In two minutes it had left the range, and was coming across the fields towards him, jumping the fences, dodging under the trees, and racing across the plain with its white mane and tail tossing as it came. It seemed to be making straight for him.

He was not really frightened — you must not think that about him — but he was just beginning to wonder if it were not nearly time to go home to dinner, when he noticed that the white horse had stopped, just at the foot of the bald hill. It was looking up at him, tossing its head and pawing the ground — the most beautiful white horse that he had ever seen, even in a circus. Then it appeared to get over its excitement and began to trot quietly up the hill toward him.

TIP of the DAY

Note the descriptive language used by the author. Which words help you to visualize the events that take place in the story?

I do not think anyone would have blamed Neville if he had decided then to go home to dinner at once. But he was rather a brave boy, and he was certainly very curious, so he just stood still and waited.

And here is where the most wonderful part of the story begins. The white horse trotted up to Neville and spoke to him. That would surprise most people; and Neville was certainly as much surprised as anyone else would have been.

"What are you frightened of?" asked the white horse in a loud voice.

Now, Neville WAS just a little frightened by this time; but he was not going to show it, so he just said, "Who's frightened?"

"You're frightened," said the white horse, louder than ever. "You're only a timid little boy. I thought when I saw you in the distance that you were one of the plucky ones; but I was mistaken. You're just a little cowardly-custard."

Exercises

1. How is the word *bald* used in the story?

   A. To describe a man's head
   B. To describe a car's tires.
   C. To describe someone's clothing.
   D. To describe a hill.

4. What does the word *timid* mean in the story?

   A. shy
   B. fearless
   C. kind
   D. small

2. What do the clouds look like to Neville?

   A. buildings
   B. toys
   C. animals
   D. people

5. What does Neville like to do while on the hill?

3. How does Neville feel when the horse comes near him?

   A. happy
   B. surprised
   C. frightened
   D. angry

6. Make a prediction. What might happen next to Neville in the story?

WEEK 2

VIDEO
EXPLANATIONS

ARGOPREP.COM

Find detailed video explanations to each problem on:
ArgoPrep.com or Download our app: **ArgoPrep Video Explanations**

Plural Nouns

CCSS.ELA-LITERACY.L.3.1.B

Nouns describe a person, place, thing, or idea. When a noun talks about more than one thing, it is known as a plural noun.

To make many nouns plural, you can simply add –s to their ending.

Here are some examples:

Matt held up a red ball.

Matt held up two red balls.

One red ball is singular, while two red balls are plural.

Mariah took her dog to see the veterinarian for a check-up.

Mariah took her dogs to see the veterinarian for a check-up.

One dog is singular, while two or more dogs are plural.

The boy went to the fair to ride the rollercoaster.

The boys went to the fair to ride the rollercoaster.

Boy is singular, while two or more boys are plural.

When deciding whether a noun is singular or plural, ask yourself: Is there only one? Or is there more than one?

Let's practice!

When adjusting from a singular to a plural noun in a sentence, reread the entire sentence to make sure that it makes sense, and that all the words within it agree with one another.

Exercises

Read each sentence and pay especially close attention to the underlined word. Then, on the lines below, identify if that word is singular or plural.

Complete the sentence by writing in a noun on the line.

1. There were two <u>dogs</u> playing fetch in the field.

    plural

    CCSS.ELA-LITERACY.L.3.1.B

4. Brenda's two __Brother__ love to going skiing.

    CCSS.ELA-LITERACY.L.3.1.B

2. Is the <u>ant</u> eating that crumb?

    singular

    CCSS.ELA-LITERACY.L.3.1.B

5. My small gray __kitten__ played with the ball of yarn.

    CCSS.ELA-LITERACY.L.3.1.B

3. I washed my mom's <u>car</u> this morning.

    sinoular

    CCSS.ELA-LITERACY.L.3.1.B

6. The old __bulb__ had burnt out and needed replaced in the lamp.

    CCSS.ELA-LITERACY.L.3.1.B

23

Special Plural Nouns

CCSS.ELA-LITERACY.L.3.1.B

Some nouns must add –es instead of -s to tell more than one. These are known as special plural nouns.

Nouns that end in ch, sh, x, o, or ss become plural by adding –es.

Nouns that end in f or fe, must drop the f or fe, and then add v and es.

Nouns that end in y, drop the y, and add –ies.

Here are some examples:

church	churches
brush	brushes
box	boxes
tomato	tomatoes
dress	dresses
knife	knives
baby	babies

When deciding the correct spelling for turning a singular noun into a plural noun, ask yourself if any of the special rules apply.

Let's practice!

TIP of the DAY

What are some other words that you are familiar with that fall into the spelling patterns listed above? How many can you think of?

Exercises

Write the plural form of each noun on the lines below.

1. bench _es_____.

4. family _s_____.

2. butterfly _s_____.

5. elf _s_____.

3. potato _s_____.

6. wish _es_____.

CCSS.ELA-LITERACY.L.3.1.B

Find detailed video explanations to each problem on:
ArgoPrep.com or Download our app: **ArgoPrep Video Explanations**

Irregular Plural Nouns

CCSS.ELA-LITERACY.L.3.1.B

Some nouns completely change their spelling to tell more than one. These are known as irregular plural nouns.

These nouns do not follow any of the previous rules. As you use them and become more familiar with them, it becomes easier to remember them.

Here are some examples:

child	children
tooth	teeth
foot	feet
woman	women
mouse	mice
goose	geese
deer	deer
moose	moose

Note that some singular nouns remain the same in their singular form and their plural form also.

Let's practice!

Irregular plural nouns do not necessarily follow a pattern, but they can be easily remembered through repetition, or using and spelling them over and over again.

Exercises

Write the plural form of each noun on the lines below.

1. sheep _S_____ .

2. person _S_____ .

3. ox _es_____ .

4. man _S_____ .

5. fish _S_____ .

6. cactus _es_____ .

WEEK 3

VIDEO
EXPLANATIONS

ARGOPREP.COM

Week 3 - Monday

Find detailed video explanations to each problem on:
ArgoPrep.com or Download our app: **ArgoPrep Video Explanations**

Excerpt from **The Conceited Pig**

One cold November evening several little pigs were lying very comfortably in their sty, and keeping themselves warm by burying their noses under the straw, when one who had been routing about very uneasily for some time gave a loud grunt all at once, and seemed to be very much frightened. His mother, the old sow, who was stretched in one corner of the sty fast asleep, opened her little brown eyes, and asked in a very angry voice what was the matter. Several of the little pigs answered at once that it was only Wilful who was making such a noise that nobody could go to sleep.

"Hush, hush, hush!" cried Wilful, as soon as his brothers were silent; "Hush! Do not you hear a great cracking and noise the other side of the yard? I am quite sure that the stables are on fire. Had not we better all go and help to put it out directly?"

"Nonsense and stuff, you foolish little fellow!" exclaimed his mother; "you are always fancying something or other is the matter, and wanting to poke your nose into things that don't concern you. I cannot hear any noise at all, and I beg you will be quiet, and let me go to sleep again."

The little pig did not dare answer his mother, so he lay quite still for a minute or two, hoping that he should hear the same noise again. And presently he did hear it, louder than before, and there could be no doubt that more than usual was going on about the premises. He looked round to see what his mother would say now; but she had fallen fast asleep again, and two or three of his brothers were snoring very loud. His little brother Fatsides was lying close to him, and Wilful thought by the twinkling of his eyes that he was not really asleep; so he gave him a kick, and said in a very low voice, for fear his mother should hear him, "Fatsides, Fatsides, do you hear? there is that strange noise come back that I heard before. Do just listen. What can it be?"

"Oh, I dare say it is nothing but the horses in the stable, or that wretched old Hector rattling his everlasting chain," answered Fatsides. "You know the other night when you woke us all up it turned out to be nothing but Buttercup rubbing her horns against the crib."

"Ah, very likely," interrupted Wilful; "but this is a very different thing. There, just hear that strange popping sound; depend upon it, either the stables are on fire, or there are a number of those frightful great blue butchers killing and carrying off all the cows. I am determined, at any rate, that I will go and see what is the matter."

"Oh, pray do not go!" exclaimed little Fatsides. "How do you know that one of the great blue butchers may not get hold of you and carry you off?"

"I should like to see them!" said Wilful. "No, no; I have lived long enough in the world to be wiser than that, too. The blue butchers will never catch me, I can tell you; clever as they think themselves, they will find that they have met with their match at last!"

When you come to a word that you are not familiar with, read the words and sentences around the word. Often times, you can find clues to help you figure out its unknown meaning.

 Find detailed video explanations to each problem on:
ArgoPrep.com or Download our app: **ArgoPrep Video Explanations**

"Well, I know you are very clever," rejoined his brother, who was getting very sleepy, "and so I suppose you must have your own way. But I do not see how you are to get out, for you know Bob always shuts the door the last thing."

"Ah, very likely," said Wilful; "but the door does not fasten tight, and I can push it open with very little trouble whenever I like. The other morning, before any of you were awake, I went out to desire Cock-a-doodle not to crow so loud, because I thought it would disturb my mother, and nobody knew anything about it; and Cock-a-doodle, by the way, behaved so extremely ill that I have taken no notice of him ever since…"

Exercises

1. How do the pigs keep warm?

   A. They rest under a blanket.
   B. They sit near the heater.
   C. They put their noses under the straw.
   D. They sleep in the sun.

   CCSS.ELA-LITERACY.RL.3.1

4. What is Wilful worried about?

   A. Being scolded
   B. Going hungry
   C. A fire
   D. A tornado

   CCSS.ELA-LITERACY.RL.3.3

2. Why were the pigs annoyed with Wilful?

   A. He was being cruel to them.
   B. He was making noises.
   C. He ate all of their food.
   D. He would not play with them.

   CCSS.ELA-LITERACY.RL.3.1

5. What is Fatsides relationship to Wilful?

   A. He is his uncle.
   B. He is his son.
   C. He is his father.
   D. He is his brother.

   CCSS.ELA-LITERACY.RL.3.2

3. Which of the following words is a synonym for *premises* in the story?

   A. house
   B. place
   C. vehicle
   D. office

   CCSS.ELA-LITERACY.RL.3.4

6. What does Fatsides fear?

   A. the butcher
   B. the farmer
   C. his mother
   D. a storm

   CCSS.ELA-LITERACY.RL.3.1

Song of the Sea
By Barry Cornwall

The sea! the sea! the open sea!
The blue, the fresh, the ever free!
Without a mark, without a bound,
It runneth the earth's wide regions round;
It plays with the clouds; it mocks the skies,
Or like a cradled creature lies.

I'm on the sea! I'm on the sea!
I am where I would ever be;
With the blue above and the blue below,
And silence wheresoe'er I go.
If a storm should come and awake the deep
What matter? I shall ride and sleep.

I love, oh, how I love to ride
On the fierce, foaming, bursting tide,
When every mad wave drowns the moon,
Or whistles aloud his tempest tune,
And tells how goeth the world below,
And why the southwest blasts do blow.

I never was on the dull, tame shore,
But I loved the great sea more and more,
And back I flew to her billowy breast,
Like a bird that seeketh its mother's nest;
And a mother she was, and is, to me,
For I was born on the open sea!

I've lived, since then, in calm and strife,
Full fifty summers a sailor's life,
With wealth to spend and a power to range,
But never have sought nor sighed for change;
And Death, whenever he comes to me,
Shall come on the wild, unbounded sea.

Poetry often incorporates language that appeals to your senses. Locate at least three words in the poem that affect one or more of your senses.

Exercises

1. Who is narrating the poem?

   A. a father
   B. a child
   C. a sailor
   D. a fisherman

4. What does the sea drown in the poem?

   A. boats
   B. the moon
   C. the shore
   D. seashells

2. How is the sea described in the poem?

   A. dull and tame
   B. wild and unbounded
   C. small and silent
   D. warm and wide

5. Which of the following is a synonym for *mocks* in the poem?

   A. sings
   B. teases
   C. cries
   D. yells

3. How many years has the narrator experienced the sea?

   A. forty
   B. thirty
   C. sixty
   D. fifty

6. Which of the following does *tempest tune* refer to in the poem?

   A. a pretty song
   B. raging waves
   C. a violent storm
   D. the cool breeze

Find detailed video explanations to each problem on:
ArgoPrep.com or Download our app: **ArgoPrep Video Explanations**

Excerpt from **Goody Gracious and the Forget-Me-Not**
By John Neal

Once there was a little bit of a thing, — not more than so high, — and her name was Ruth Page; but they called her Teenty-Tawnty, for she was the daintiest little creature you ever saw, with the smoothest hair and the brightest face; and then she was always playing about, and always happy; and so the people that lived in that part of the country, when they heard her laughing and singing all by herself at peep of day, like little birds after a shower, and saw her running about in the edge of the wood after tulips and butterflies, or tumbling head-over-heels in the long rich grass by the river-side, with her little pet lamb or her two white pigeons always under her feet, or listening to the wild bees in the apple-blossoms, with her sweet mouth "all in a tremble," and her happy eyes brimful of sunshine, — they used to say that she was no child at all, or no child of earth, but a fairy-gift, and that she must have been dropped into her mother's lap, like a handful of flowers, when she was half asleep; and so they wouldn't call her Ruth Page, — no indeed, that they wouldn't! — but they called her little Teenty-Tawnty, or the Little Fairy; and they used to bring her fairy tales to read, till she couldn't bear to read anything else, and wanted to be a fairy herself.

Well, and so one day, when she was out in the sweet-smelling woods, all alone by herself, singing, "Where are you going, my pretty maid, my pretty maid?" and watching the gold-jackets, and the blue dragon-flies, and the sweet pond-lilies, and the bright-eyed glossy eels, and the little crimson-spotted fish, as they "coiled and swam," and darted hither and thither, like "flashes of golden fire," and then huddled together, all of a sudden, just underneath the green turf where she sat, as if they saw something, and were half frightened to death, and were trying to hide in the shadow; well and so — as she sat there, with her little feet hanging over and almost touching the water, singing to herself, "My face is my fortune, sir, she said! sir, she said!" and looking down into a deep sunshiny spot, and holding the soft smooth hair away from her face with both hands, and trying to count the dear little fish before they got over their fright, all at once she began to think of the water-fairies, and how cool and pleasant it must be to live in these deep sunshiny hollows, with green turf all about you, the blossoming trees and the blue skies overhead, the bright gravel underneath your feet, like powdered stars, and thousands of beautiful fish for playfellows! all spotted with gold and crimson, or winged with rose-leaves, and striped with faint purple and burnished silver, like the shells and flowers of the deep sea, where the moonlight buds and blossoms forever and ever; and then she thought if she could only just reach over, and dip one of her little fat rosy feet into the smooth shining water, — just once — only once, — it would be so pleasant and she should be so happy and then, if she could but manage to scare the fishes a little, — a very little, — that would be such glorious fun, too, — wouldn't it, you?

Well and so — she kept stooping and stooping, and stretching and stretching, and singing to herself all the while, "Sir, she said! sir, she said! I'm going a milking, sir, she said!" till just as she was ready to tumble in, head first, something jumped out of the bushes behind her, almost touching her as it passed, and went plump into the deepest part of the pool saying, "Once! Once!" with a heavy booming sound, like the tolling of a great bell under water, and afar off.

Authors often use dialogue that reflects the language used during the time period that a story takes place. Do you notice any words in this story that reflect language used many years ago?

"Goody gracious! What's that?" screamed little Ruth Page, and then, the very next moment, she began to laugh and jump and clap her hands, to see what a scampering there was among the poor silly fish, and all for nothing! said she; for out came a great good-natured bull-frog, with an eye like a bird, and a big bell-mouth, and a back all frosted over with precious stones, and dripping with sunshine; and there he sat looking at her awhile, as if he wanted to frighten her away; and then he opened his great lubberly mouth at her, and bellowed out, "Once! Once!" and vanished.

"Luddy tuddy! Who cares for you?" said little Ruth; and so, having got over her fright, she began to creep to the edge of the bank once more, and look down into the deep water, to see what had become of the little fish that were so plentiful there, and so happy but a few minutes before. But they were all gone, and the water was as still as death; and while she sat looking into it, and waiting for them to come back, and wondering why they should be so frightened at nothing but a bull-frog, which they must have seen a thousand times, the poor little simpletons and thinking she should like to catch one of the smallest and carry it home to her little baby-brother, all at once a soft shadow fell upon the water, and the scented wind blew her smooth hair all into her eyes, and as she put up both hands in a hurry to pull it away, she heard something like a whisper close to her ear, saying, "Twice! twice!" and just then the trailing branch of a tree swept over the turf, and filled the whole air with a storm of blossoms, and she heard the same low whisper repeated close at her ear, saying, "Twice! Twice!" and then she happened to look down into the water,--and what do you think she saw there?

"Goody gracious, mamma! Is that you?" said poor little Ruth; and up she jumped, screaming louder than ever, and looking all about her, and calling, "Mamma, mamma! I see you, mamma! You needn't hide, mamma!" But no mamma was to be found.

Exercises

1. What does the word *daintiest* mean in the story?

   A. thin
   B. delicate
   C. flat
   D. long

   CCSS.ELA-LITERACY.RL.3.4

4. What does Ruth Page see?

   A. a rainbow
   B. a troll
   C. a fish
   D. a fairy

   CCSS.ELA-LITERACY.RL.3.4

2. What did Teenty-Tawnty want to be?

   A. a teacher
   B. a fairy
   C. a doctor
   D. a witch

   CCSS.ELA-LITERACY.RL.3.1

5. What does Teenty-Tawnty do in the woods?

   Plat

   CCSS.ELA-LITERACY.RL.3.3

3. How can you describe the tree in the story?

   A. flowering
   B. bare
   C. sprouting
   D. decaying

   CCSS.ELA-LITERACY.RL.3.4

6. Make a prediction. What do you think will happen next in the story?

   She will see another bullfrog.

   CCSS.ELA-LITERACY.RL.3.5

WEEK 4

VIDEO
EXPLANATIONS

ARGOPREP.COM

Concrete Nouns

CCSS.ELA-LITERACY.L.3.1.C

Nouns name a person place, thing, or idea. Nouns that are physical and can be experienced with one or more or your five senses are known as concrete nouns.

Here are some examples. Think about the sense(s) that correspond(s) with them.

ice cream
puppies
sunshine
candy
shoes
water
grass
car
book

Which senses did you think of when you read the list? These are all physical concrete nouns.

Let's practice!

Nouns are a basic building block of our sentences. Concrete nouns are usually quite simple and we need them to form complete thoughts.

Exercises

Read the sentences. Look at the underlined noun in each. Write one or more senses on the line that corresponds to each noun.

1. Jenna loves to go to the <u>beach</u>.

   Sight, sound

4. The <u>penguin</u> waddled on the ice.

   see

2. The <u>snow</u> fell from the sky.

   sight, sound,
   feel

5. The <u>cake</u> had red candles on it.

   taste

3. We went to the movies and ate <u>popcorn</u>.

   Taste

6. The <u>airplane</u> was ready for take off.

   hear

Find detailed video explanations to each problem on:
ArgoPrep.com or Download our app: **ArgoPrep Video Explanations**

Abstract Nouns

CCSS.ELA-LITERACY.L.3.1.C

Nouns that cannot be experienced by one or more of your five senses are known as abstract nouns. These nouns cannot be seen, touched, heard, smelled, or tasted.

Here are some examples:

love

friendship

faith

peace

jealousy

truth

wisdom

loyalty

honesty

joy

Abstract nouns cannot be touched or grasped. They do not have any kind of physical appearance or appeal to specific senses.

Let's practice!

Abstract nouns focus on things that cannot be seen. Can you make a list of abstract nouns that you might incorporate into your writing?

Exercises

Identify the abstract noun in each sentence below and circle it.

1. Jessica was filled with (joy) when the music began.

CCSS.ELA-LITERACY.L.3.1.C

2. His (kindness) was appreciated by all.

CCSS.ELA-LITERACY.L.3.1.C

3. The children showed their (pride) as they saluted the flag.

CCSS.ELA-LITERACY.L.3.1.C

4. His (loyalty) was obvious when he placed his vote.

CCSS.ELA-LITERACY.L.3.1.C

5. Her (brilliance) led to the new invention.

CCSS.ELA-LITERACY.L.3.1.C

6. His (bravery) was helpful during the difficult situation.

CCSS.ELA-LITERACY.L.3.1.C

Find detailed video explanations to each problem on:
ArgoPrep.com or Download our app: **ArgoPrep Video Explanations**

Concrete and Abstract Nouns

CCSS.ELA-LITERACY.L.3.1.C

Let's review. Nouns name a person place, thing, or idea.

Nouns that are physical and can be experienced with one or more or your five senses are known as concrete nouns.

Nouns that cannot be experienced by one or more of your five senses are known as abstract nouns. These nouns cannot be seen, touched, heard, smelled, or tasted.

Look at some examples in the chart below.

Concrete:	Abstract:
sunshine	happiness
candy	love
bird	loyalty
truck	faith
pencil	brilliance

Ask yourself whether or not the noun can be experienced with your senses. Nouns that can are concrete, while nouns that cannot are abstract.

Let's practice!

There are several different types of nouns. List the various types you know and examples of each. Categorizing them can help you to understand and use them correctly.

Exercises

Circle each abstract noun(s) in each sentence. Underline the concrete noun(s).

1. My dad's anger came about after I lost his favorite baseball.

CCSS.ELA-LITERACY.L.3.1.C

4. The teacher's humor kept her students laughing.

CCSS.ELA-LITERACY.L.3.1.C

2. Her love for children always shines through.

CCSS.ELA-LITERACY.L.3.1.C

5. I wished Joe luck as he left for his big game.

CCSS.ELA-LITERACY.L.3.1.C

3. My grandpa is full of wisdom.

CCSS.ELA-LITERACY.L.3.1.C

6. Her honesty helped the police officer.

CCSS.ELA-LITERACY.L.3.1.C

WEEK 5

VIDEO
EXPLANATIONS

ARGOPREP.COM

Week 5 - Monday

Find detailed video explanations to each problem on:
ArgoPrep.com or Download our app: **ArgoPrep Video Explanations**

Excerpt from **East of the Sun and West of the Moon**

Once upon a time there was a poor husbandman who had many children and little to give them in the way either of food or clothing. They were all pretty, but the prettiest of all was the youngest daughter, who was so beautiful that there were no bounds to her beauty.

So once — it was late on a Thursday evening in autumn, and wild weather outside, terribly dark, and raining so heavily and blowing so hard that the walls of the cottage shook again — they were all sitting together by the fireside, each of them busy with something or other, when suddenly some one rapped three times against the window-pane. The man went out to see what could be the matter, and when he got out there stood a great big white bear.

"Good-evening to you," said the White Bear.

"Good-evening," said the man.

"Will you give me your youngest daughter?" said the White Bear; "if you will, you shall be as rich as you are now poor."

Truly the man would have had no objection to be rich, but he thought to himself: "I must first ask my daughter about this," so he went in and told them that there was a great white bear outside who had faithfully promised to make them all rich if he might but have the youngest daughter.

She said no, and would not hear of it; so the man went out again, and settled with the White Bear that he should come again next Thursday evening, and get her answer. Then the man persuaded her, and talked so much to her about the wealth that they would have, and what a good thing it would be for herself, that at last she made up her mind to go, and washed and mended all her rags, made herself as smart as she could, and held herself in readiness to set out. Little enough had she to take away with her.

Next Thursday evening the White Bear came to fetch her. She seated herself on his back with her bundle, and thus they departed. When they had gone a great part of the way, the White Bear said: "Are you afraid?"

"No, that I am not," said she.

"Keep tight hold of my fur, and then there is no danger," said he.

And thus she rode far, far away, until they came to a great mountain.

Then the White Bear knocked on it, and a door opened, and they went into a castle where there were many brilliantly lighted rooms which shone with gold and silver, likewise a large hall in which there was a well-spread table, and it was so magnificent that it would be hard to make anyone understand how splendid it was. The White Bear gave her a silver bell, and told her that when she needed anything she had but to ring this bell, and what she wanted would appear. So after she had eaten, and night was drawing near, she grew sleepy after her journey, and thought she would like to go to bed. She rang the bell, and scarcely had she touched it before she found herself in a chamber where a bed stood ready made for her, which was as pretty as anyone could wish to sleep in. It had pillows of silk, and curtains of silk fringed with gold, and everything that was in the room was of gold or silver, but when she had lain down and put out the light a man came and lay down beside her, and behold it was the White Bear, who cast off the form of a beast during the night.

TIP of the DAY

The main character in the story is the person or animal that the story is mostly about. Can you identify the main character in the excerpt above?

She never saw him, however, for he always came after she had put out her light, and went away before daylight appeared.

So all went well and happily for a time, but then she began to be very sad and sorrowful, for all day long she had to go about alone; and she did so wish to go home to her father and mother and brothers and sisters. Then the White Bear asked what it was that she wanted, and she told him that it was so dull there in the mountain, and that she had to go about all alone, and that in her parents' house at home there were all her brothers and sisters, and it was because she could not go to that she was so sorrowful.

Exercises

1. How is the youngest daughter described in the story?

   A. dainty
   B. beautiful
   C. unkind
   D. lazy

4. Why does the visitor return?

   A. The father asks him for more time.
   B. He likes to visit.
   C. He comes for dinner each Thursday.
   D. He needs to get money.

2. Who comes to the door?

   A. another child
   B. a troll
   C. a white bear
   D. a witch

5. What does the visitor want?

   A. money
   B. food
   C. the youngest daughter
   D. a house to live in

3. Which of the following words describes the visitor?

   A. adamant
   B. cruel
   C. small
   D. lazy

6. Why is the youngest daughter sorrowful?

   A. She is scared.
   B. She is tired.
   C. She is lonely.
   D. She is angry.

Week 5 - Wednesday

Find detailed video explanations to each problem on:
ArgoPrep.com or Download our app: **ArgoPrep Video Explanations**

Excerpt from **The Master-Maid**

Once upon a time there was a king who had many sons. I do not exactly know how many there were, but the youngest of them could not stay quietly at home, and was determined to go out into the world and try his luck, and after a long time the King was forced to give him leave to go. When he had traveled about for several days, he came to a giant's house, and hired himself to the giant as a servant. In the morning the giant had to go out to pasture his goats, and as he was leaving the house he told the King's son that he must clean out the stable. "And after you have done that," he said, "you need not do any more work to-day, for you have come to a kind master, and that you shall find. But what I set you to do must be done both well and thoroughly, and you must on no account go into any of the rooms, which lead out of the room in which you slept last night. If you do, I will take your life."

"Well to be sure, he is an easy master!" said the Prince to himself as he walked up and down the room humming and singing, for he thought there would be plenty of time left to clean out the stable; "but it would be amusing to steal a glance into his other rooms as well," thought the Prince, "for there must be something that he is afraid of my seeing, as I am not allowed to enter them." So he went into the first room. A cauldron was hanging from the walls; it was boiling, but the Prince could see no fire under it. "I wonder what is inside it," he thought, and dipped a lock of his hair in, and the hair became just as if it were all made of copper. "That's a nice kind of soup. If anyone were to taste that his throat would be gilded," said the youth, and then he went into the next chamber. There, too, a cauldron was hanging from the wall, bubbling and boiling, but there was no fire under this either. "I will just try what this is like too," said the Prince, thrusting another lock of his hair into it, and it came out silvered over. "Such costly soup is not to be had in my father's palace," said the Prince; "but everything depends on how it tastes," and then he went into the third room. There, too, a cauldron was hanging from the wall, boiling, exactly the same as in the two other rooms, and the Prince took pleasure in trying this also, so he dipped a lock of hair in, and it came out so brightly gilded that it shone again. "Some talk about going from bad to worse," said the Prince; "but this is better and better. If he boils gold here, what can he boil in there?" He was determined to see, and went through the door into the fourth room. No cauldron was to be seen there, but on a bench someone was seated who was like a king's daughter, but, whosoever she was, she was so beautiful that never in the Prince's life had he seen her equal.

"Oh! in heaven's name what are you doing here?" said she who sat upon the bench.

"I took the place of servant here yesterday," said the Prince.

"May you soon have a better place, if you have come to serve here!" said she.

"Oh, but I think I have got a kind master," said the Prince. "He has not given me hard work to do to-day. When I have cleaned out the stable I shall be done."

"Yes, but how will you be able to do that?" she asked again. "If you clean it out as other people do, ten pitchforks-full will come in for every one you throw out. But I will teach you how to do it; you must turn your pitchfork upside down, and work with the handle, and then all will fly out of its own accord."

Thinking about the qualities of a character can help you to understand his or her actions. What personality traits does the Prince have in this story?

"Yes, I will attend to that," said the Prince, and stayed sitting where he was the whole day, for it was soon settled between them that they would marry each other, he and the King's daughter; so the first day of his service with the giant did not seem long to him. But when evening was drawing near she said that it would now be better for him to clean out the stable before the giant came home. When he got there he had a fancy to try if what she had said were true, so he began to work in the same way that he had seen the stable-boys doing in his father's stables, but he soon saw that he must give up that, for when he had worked a very short time he had scarcely any room left to stand. So he did what the Princess had taught him, turned the pitchfork round, and worked with the handle, and in the twinkling of an eye the stable was as clean as if it had been scoured. When he had done that, he went back again into the room in which the giant had given him leave to stay, and there he walked backward and forward on the floor, and began to hum and sing.

Exercises

1. What does the youngest son decide to do?

   A. Open a store
   B. Go out into the world
   C. Live at home
   D. Plant crops and begin farming

   CCSS.ELA-LITERACY.RL.3.1

2. Who does he meet?

   A. a blacksmith
   B. a farmer
   C. a troll
   D. a giant

   CCSS.ELA-LITERACY.RL.3.1

3. Which of the following is a synonym for *cauldron*?

   A. a pot
   B. a vase
   C. a fireplace
   D. a heater

   CCSS.ELA-LITERACY.RL.3.4

4. What type of food is cooking?

   A. a roast
   B. soup
   C. cookies
   D. pasta

   CCSS.ELA-LITERACY.RL.3.3

5. What is a pitchfork?

   A. a tool for eating
   B. a tool for gardening
   C. a tool for painting
   D. a tool for cleaning

   CCSS.ELA-LITERACY.RL.3.4

6. Which word can replace the word *scoured* in the story?

   A. scrubbed
   B. dried
   C. lifted
   D. placed

   CCSS.ELA-LITERACY.RL.3.4

Notes

Find detailed video explanations to each problem on:
ArgoPrep.com or Download our app: **ArgoPrep Video Explanations**

Excerpt from **The Water-Lily: The Gold-Spinners**

Once upon a time, in a large forest, there lived an old woman and three maidens. They were all three beautiful, but the youngest was the fairest. Their hut was quite hidden by trees, and none saw their beauty but the sun by day, and the moon by night, and the eyes of the stars. The old woman kept the girls hard at work, from morning till night, spinning gold flax into yarn, and when one distaff was empty another was given them, so they had no rest. The thread had to be fine and even, and when done was locked up in a secret chamber by the old woman, who twice or thrice every summer went a journey. Before she went she gave out work for each day of her absence, and always returned in the night, so that the girls never saw what she brought back with her, neither would she tell them whence the gold flax came, nor what it was to be used for.

Now, when the time came round for the old woman to set out on one of these journeys, she gave each maiden work for six days, with the usual warning: "Children, don't let your eyes wander, and on no account speak to a man, for, if you do, your thread will lose its brightness, and misfortunes of all kinds will follow." They laughed at this oft-repeated caution, saying to each other: "How can our gold thread lose its brightness, and have we any chance of speaking to a man?"

On the third day after the old woman's departure a young prince, hunting in the forest, got separated from his companions, and completely lost. Weary of seeking his way, he flung himself down under a tree, leaving his horse to browse at will, and fell asleep.

The sun had set when he awoke and began once more to try and find his way out of the forest. At last he perceived a narrow foot-path, which he eagerly followed and found that it led him to a small hut. The maidens, who were sitting at the door of their hut for coolness, saw him approaching, and the two elder were much alarmed, for they remembered the old woman's warning; but the youngest said: "Never before have I seen anyone like him; let me have one look." They entreated her to come in, but, seeing that she would not, left her, and the Prince, coming up, courteously greeted the maiden, and told her he had lost his way in the forest and was both hungry and weary. She set food before him, and was so delighted with his conversation that she forgot the old woman's caution, and lingered for hours. In the meantime the Prince's companions sought him far and wide, but to no purpose, so they sent two messengers to tell the sad news to the King, who immediately ordered a regiment of cavalry and one of infantry to go and look for him.

After three days' search, they found the hut. The Prince was still sitting by the door and had been so happy in the maiden's company that the time had seemed like a single hour. Before leaving he promised to return and fetch her to his father's court, where he would make her his bride. When he had gone, she sat down to her wheel to make up for lost time, but was dismayed to find that her thread had lost all its brightness. Her heart beat fast and she wept bitterly, for she remembered the old woman's warning and knew not what misfortune might now befall her.

The old woman returned in the night and knew by the tarnished thread what had happened in her absence. She was furiously angry and told the maiden that she had brought down misery both on herself and on the Prince. The maiden could not rest for thinking of this. At last she could bear it no longer, and resolved to seek help from the Prince.

Stories that begin with "Once upon a time" are often fairy tales. Fairy tales contain made up fantasy-like elements.

As a child she had learned to understand the speech of birds, and this was now of great use to her, for, seeing a raven pluming itself on a pine bough, she cried softly to it: "Dear bird, cleverest of all birds, as well as swiftest on wing, wilt thou help me?" "How can I help thee?" asked the raven. She answered: "Fly away, until thou comest to a splendid town, where stands a king's palace; seek out the king's son and tell him that a great misfortune has befallen me." Then she told the raven how her thread had lost its brightness, how terribly angry the old woman was, and how she feared some great disaster. The raven promised faithfully to do her bidding, and, spreading its wings, flew away. The maiden now went home and worked hard all day at winding up the yarn her elder sisters had spun, for the old woman would let her spin no longer. Toward evening she heard the raven's "craa, craa," from the pine tree and eagerly hastened thither to hear the answer.

By great good fortune the raven had found a wind wizard's son in the palace garden, who understood the speech of birds, and to him he had entrusted the message. When the Prince heard it, he was very sorrowful, and took counsel with his friends how to free the maiden. Then he said to the wind wizard's son: "Beg the raven to fly quickly back to the maiden and tell her to be ready on the ninth night, for then will I come and fetch her away." The wind wizard's son did this, and the raven flew so swiftly that it reached the hut that same evening. The maiden thanked the bird heartily and went home, telling no one what she had heard.

As the ninth night drew near she became very unhappy, for she feared lest some terrible mischance should arise and ruin all. On this night she crept quietly out of the house and waited trembling at some little distance from the hut. Presently she heard the muffled tramp of horses, and soon the armed troop appeared, led by the Prince, who had prudently marked all the trees beforehand, in order to know the way. When he saw the maiden he sprang from his horse, lifted her into the saddle, and then, mounting behind, rode homeward. The moon shone so brightly that they had no difficulty in seeing the marked trees.

Exercises

1. Where did the old woman live?

   A. in a hut
   B. in a cave in the mountains
   C. in an apartment
   D. in a houseboat

4. Who appears on the ninth night?

   A. a troll
   B. a raven
   C. a prince
   D. the mother

2. What must the girls do?

   A. cook the food
   B. clean their home
   C. spin thread
   D. wash the clothes

5. What does the prince do to the maiden?

3. What does the maiden know how to do?

   A. Sew clothing
   B. Speak to the birds
   C. Make dinner
   D. Build a new home

6. What might happen next in the story?

WEEK 6

VIDEO
EXPLANATIONS

ARGOPREP.COM

Find detailed video explanations to each problem on:
ArgoPrep.com or Download our app: **ArgoPrep Video Explanations**

Present Tense Verbs

CCSS.ELA-LITERACY.L.3.1.E

A verb that tells what happens now is known as a present tense verb.

If the subject is singular, add –s to most verbs.

If the subject is plural, do not add –s or –es. This also applies when the subject is I, you, we, or they.

   Here are some examples:

      She plays.

      He runs.

      I talk.

      You listen.

      Chase dreams.

      She teaches.

Verbs that tell about an action that is currently happening are known as present tense verbs.

Let's practice!

Remember that a verb should always agree with the subject of the sentence.

56

Exercises

Choose the correct form of the present tense verb to complete each sentence.

1. The two girls (play / plays) a game of tag.

4. Everyone (look/ looks) at the parade passing by.

2. My dad (worry / worries) about being late for work.

5. Jim (order / orders) an ice cream sundae.

3. She (put / puts) the markers back in the box.

6. I (need / needs) to go to the grocery store.

Find detailed video explanations to each problem on:
ArgoPrep.com or Download our app: **ArgoPrep Video Explanations**

Past Tense Verbs

CCSS.ELA-LITERACY.L.3.1.E

A verb that tells what already happened is known as a past tense verb.

Add –ed to most verbs to show past tense.

Some examples are listed below.

I walk to the store. (present)
I walked to the store. (past)

Brenda jumps in the pool. (present)
Brenda jumped in the pool. (past)

Joe opens the trunk of the car. (present)
Joe opened the trunk of the car. (past)

The kids like the field trip. (present)
The kids liked the field trip. (past)

Past tense verbs usually end in -ed.

Let's practice!

TIP of the DAY

Understanding the different verb tenses will allow you to write in all tenses. You can easily change the tense of a sentence to fit your thoughts correctly.

Exercises

Complete the sentence by adding a verb in the past tense form.

1. The man _____ the garage.

CCSS.ELA-LITERACY.L.3.1.E

4. The children _____ with the toys.

CCSS.ELA-LITERACY.L.3.1.E

2. Lila _____ a flower from the garden.

CCSS.ELA-LITERACY.L.3.1.E

5. George _____ to the man about his day.

CCSS.ELA-LITERACY.L.3.1.E

3. Michael _____ on the sidewalk.

CCSS.ELA-LITERACY.L.3.1.E

6. Wesley _____ until five o'clock.

CCSS.ELA-LITERACY.L.3.1.E

Find detailed video explanations to each problem on:
ArgoPrep.com or Download our app: **ArgoPrep Video Explanations**

Future Tense Verbs

CCSS.ELA-LITERACY.L.3.1.E

A future tense verb tells about an action that is going to happen.

The special verb *will* helps us to tell about the future.

Some examples are listed below.

I walk to the store. (present)

I walked to the store. (past)

I will walk to the store. (future)

Brenda jumps in the pool. (present)

Brenda jumped in the pool. (past)

Brenda will jump in the pool. (future)

Joe opens the trunk of the car. (present)

Joe opened the trunk of the car. (past)

Joe will open the trunk of the car. (future)

The kids like the field trip. (present)

The kids liked the field trip. (past)

The kids will like the field trip. (future)

Add the word *will* in front of a verb to change its tense to future tense.

Let's practice!

Future tense verbs are often used in advertisements. Can you think of a radio, television, or newspaper ad that incorporates a future tense verb?

Exercises

Complete the sentence by adding a verb in the future tense form.

1. The football team _____ a game.

CCSS.ELA-LITERACY.L.3.1.E

4. Shana _____ to Florida soon.

CCSS.ELA-LITERACY.L.3.1.E

2. Edith _____ for her test.

CCSS.ELA-LITERACY.L.3.1.E

5. The birds _____ south for the winter.

CCSS.ELA-LITERACY.L.3.1.E

3. They _____ to the movies tomorrow.

CCSS.ELA-LITERACY.L.3.1.E

6. Ben's truck _____ in the garage.

CCSS.ELA-LITERACY.L.3.1.E

WEEK 7

VIDEO EXPLANATIONS

ARGOPREP.COM

Find detailed video explanations to each problem on:
ArgoPrep.com or Download our app: **ArgoPrep Video Explanations**

Excerpt from **The Gold-Children**

There was once a poor man and a poor woman who had nothing but a little cottage. They earned their bread by fishing, and always lived from hand to mouth.

But it came to pass one day, when the man was sitting by the waterside and casting his net that he drew out a fish entirely of gold.

As he was looking at the fish, full of astonishment, it began to speak and said, "Hark you, Fisherman, if you will throw me back again into the water, I will change your little hut into a splendid castle."

Then the fisherman answered, "Of what use is a castle to me, if I have nothing to eat?"

The Gold Fish continued, "That shall be taken care of. There will be a cupboard in the castle in which, when you open it, shall be dishes of the most delicate meats, and as many of them as you may desire."

"If that be true," said the man, "then I can well do you a favor."

"Yes," said the Fish, "there is, however, the condition that you shall tell no one in the world, whosoever he may be, whence your good luck has come. If you speak but one single word, all will be over."

Then the man threw the wonderful Fish back again into the water, and went home.

Where his hovel had formerly stood, now stood a great castle. He opened wide his eyes, entered, and saw his wife dressed in beautiful clothes, sitting in a splendid room.

She was quite delighted, and said, "Husband, how has all this come to pass? It suits me very well."

"Yes," said the man, "it suits me too. But I am frightfully hungry, just give me something to eat."

Said the wife, "But I have got nothing and don't know where to find anything in this new house."

"There is no need of your knowing," said the man, "for I see yonder a great cupboard, just unlock it."

When she opened it, lo! there stood cakes, meat, fruit, wine.

Then the woman cried joyfully, "What more can you want, my dear?" and they sat down, and ate and drank together.

When they had had enough, the woman said, "But, Husband, whence come all these riches?"

"Alas," answered he, "do not question me about it, for I dare not tell you anything. If I disclose it to any one, then all our good fortune will fly."

"Very good," said she, "if I am not to know anything, then I do not want to know anything."

However, she was not in earnest. She never rested day or night, and she goaded her husband until in his impatience he revealed that all was owing to a wonderful Gold Fish, which he had caught, and to which in return he had given its liberty.

And as soon as the secret was out, the splendid castle with the cupboard immediately disappeared. They were once more in the old fisherman's hut, and the man was obliged to follow his former trade and fish.

The Fish in this story talks. What does this tell you about the story's genre?

But fortune would so have it, that he once more drew out the Gold Fish.

"Listen," said the Fish, "if you will throw me back into the water again, I will once more give you the castle with the cupboard full of roast and boiled meats. Only be firm; for your life's sake don't reveal from whom you have it, or you will lose it all again!"

"I will take good care," answered the fisherman, and threw the fish back into the water.

Now at home, everything was once more in its former magnificence. The wife was overjoyed at their good fortune. But curiosity left her no peace, so that after a couple of days she began to ask again how it had come to pass, and how he had managed to secure it.

The man kept silence for a short time, but at last she made him so angry that he broke out and betrayed the secret. In an instant the castle disappeared, and they were back again in their old hut.

"Now you have got what you want," said he; "and we can gnaw at a bare bone again."

"Ah," said the woman, "I had rather have no riches; if I am not to know from whom they come, then I have no peace."

The man went back to fish, and after a while he chanced to draw out the Gold Fish for a third time.

"Listen," said the Fish, "I see very well that I am fated to fall into your hands. Take me home and cut me into six pieces. Give your wife two of them to eat, two to your horse, and bury two of them in the ground. Then they will bring you a blessing."

The fisherman took the Fish home with him, and did as it had bidden him.

It came to pass that from the two pieces that were buried in the ground, two Golden Lilies sprang up; that the horse had two Golden Foals; and the fisherman's wife bore two children who were made entirely of gold.

The children grew up, became tall and handsome, and the lilies and horses grew likewise.

Then the lads said, "Father, we want to mount our Golden Steeds and travel out in the world."

But he answered sorrowfully, "How shall I bear it, if you go away and I know not how it fares with you?"

Then they said, "The two Golden Lilies remain here. By them you may see how it is with us. If they are fresh, then we are in health. If they are withered, we are ill. If they perish, then we are dead."

Exercises

1. Why does the man in the story fish?

   A. He likes to eat them.
   B. He earns money from fishing.
   C. He loves being by the water.
   D. He is bored.

   CCSS.ELA-LITERACY.RL.3.3

2. What does the fish tell him to do?

   A. Take him to the castle
   B. Throw him back in the water
   C. Take him to the market
   D. Get new fishing bait

   CCSS.ELA-LITERACY.RL.3.1

3. What does the fish tell the man NOT to do?

   A. Tell anyone the secrets he shared
   B. Put him back into the water
   C. Leave him alone
   D. Bring his wife to see him

   CCSS.ELA-LITERACY.RL.3.3

4. What happens to the man's house?

   A. It becomes a castle.
   B. It burns down.
   C. It disappears.
   D. It fills with gold coins.

   CCSS.ELA-LITERACY.RL.3.1

5. Which word means the same as *fortune* in the story?

   A. luck
   B. vacation
   C. cash
   D. family

   CCSS.ELA-LITERACY.RL.3.4

6. Which of the following is another verb that could replace the word *perish* in the story?

   A. grow
   B. eat
   C. live
   D. die

   CCSS.ELA-LITERACY.RL.3.4

Week 7 - Wednesday

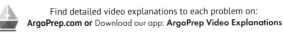

Find detailed video explanations to each problem on:
ArgoPrep.com or Download our app: **ArgoPrep Video Explanations**

Excerpt from **The Singing, Soaring Lark**

There was once on a time, a man who was about to set out on a long journey. At parting he asked his three daughters what he should bring back for them.

Whereupon the eldest wished for pearls, the second wished for diamonds, but the third said, "Dear Father, I should like a Singing, Soaring Lark."

The father said, "Yes, if I can get it, you shall have it," kissed all three, and set out.

Now, when the time had come for him to return home, he had brought pearls and diamonds for the two eldest. But he had sought everywhere in vain for a Singing, Soaring Lark for the youngest, and he was very unhappy about it, for she was his favorite child.

Then his road lay through a forest, and in the midst of it was a splendid castle. Near the castle stood a tree, and quite on the top of the tree, he saw a Singing, Soaring Lark.

"Aha, you come just at the right moment!" he said, quite delighted, and called to his servant to climb up and catch the little creature.

But as he approached the tree, a Lion leapt from beneath it, shook himself, and roared till the leaves on the tree trembled. "He who tries to steal my Singing, Soaring Lark," he cried, "will I devour."

Then the man said, "I did not know that the bird belonged to you. I will make amends for the wrong I have done, and ransom myself with a large sum of money, only spare my life."

The Lion said, "Nothing can save you, unless you will promise to give me for mine own what first meets you on your return home. But if you will do that, I will grant you your life, and you shall have the bird for your daughter, into the bargain."

The man hesitated and said, "That might be my youngest daughter, she loves me best, and always runs to meet me on my return home."

The servant, however, was terrified and said, "Why should your daughter be the very one to meet you, it might as easily be a cat, or dog?"

Then the man allowed himself to be persuaded, took the Singing, Soaring Lark, and promised to give the Lion whatsoever should first meet him on his return home.

When he reached home and entered his house, the first who met him was no other than his youngest and dearest daughter, who came running up, kissed and embraced him. When she saw that he had brought with him a Singing, Soaring Lark, she was beside herself with joy.

The father, however, could not rejoice, but began to weep, and said, "My dearest Child, I have bought the little bird at a great cost! In return for it, I have been obliged to promise you to a savage Lion. When he has you he will tear you in pieces and devour you," and he told her all, just as it had happened, and begged her not to go thither, come what might.

TIP of the DAY

Try replacing an unknown word with a known word that might mean the same thing in a sentence. Sometimes this can help you to determine if your guess about the word's meaning is correct. Does the sentence make sense with the replaced word?

But she consoled him and said, "Dearest Father, indeed your promise must be fulfilled. I will go thither and soften the Lion, so that I may return to you safely."

Next morning, she had the road pointed out to her, took leave, and went fearlessly out into the forest. The Lion, however, was an enchanted Prince and was by day a Lion, and all his people were Lions with him. But in the night, they resumed their natural human shapes.

On her arrival, she was kindly received and led into the castle. When night came, the Lion turned into a handsome man, and their wedding was celebrated with great magnificence. They lived happily together, remained awake at night, and slept in the daytime.

One day, he came and said, "Tomorrow there is a feast in your father's house, because your eldest sister is to be married, and if you are inclined to go there, my Lions shall conduct you."

She said, "Yes, I should very much like to see my father again," and went thither, accompanied by the Lions.

Exercises

1. What does the second daughter wish for in the story?

   A. diamonds
   B. a lark
   C. pearls
   D. gold

   CCSS.ELA-LITERACY.RL.3.1

4. Where does the man see a lark?

   A. in the deep forest
   B. on top of the mountain
   C. by the castle
   D. near the ocean

   CCSS.ELA-LITERACY.RL.3.1

2. What does the man have trouble finding?

   A. a lark
   B. diamonds
   C. gold
   D. pearls

   CCSS.ELA-LITERACY.RL.3.1

5. Which of the following could replace the word *enchanted* in the story?

   A. kind
   B. eager
   C. excited
   D. magical

   CCSS.ELA-LITERACY.RL.3.4

3. What appears from behind the tree?

   A. a lark
   B. a lion
   C. a fairy
   D. a woman

   CCSS.ELA-LITERACY.RL.3.3

6. What happens to the lion?

   A. He falls from a cliff.
   B. He turns into a prince.
   C. He steals the daughter.
   D. He locks himself in the castle.

   CCSS.ELA-LITERACY.RL.3.3

Find detailed video explanations to each problem on:
ArgoPrep.com or Download our app: **ArgoPrep Video Explanations**

Excerpt from **The Hedge-King**

In former days, every sound had its meaning, the birds also had their own language which every one understood. Now it only sounds like chirping, screeching, and whistling, and to some, like music without words.

It came into the birds' mind, however, that they would no longer be without a ruler, and would choose one of themselves to be King.

One alone amongst them, the green plover, was opposed to this. He had lived free and would die free, and anxiously flying hither and thither, he cried, "Where shall I go? Where shall I go?" He retired into a lonely and unfrequented marsh, and showed himself no more among his fellows.

The birds now wished to discuss the matter, and on a fine May morning they all gathered together from the woods and fields: eagles and chaffinches, owls and crows, larks and sparrows, how can I name them all? Even the cuckoo came, and the hoopoe, his clerk, who is so called because he is always heard a few days before him, and a very small bird which as yet had no name, mingled with the band.

The hen, which by some accident had heard nothing of the whole matter, was astonished at the great assemblage. "What, what, what is going to be done?" she cackled. But the cock calmed his beloved hen, and said, "Only rich people," and told her what they had on hand.

It was decided, however, that the one who could fly the highest should be King. A tree-frog which was sitting among the bushes, when he heard that, cried a warning, "No, no, no! no!" because he thought that many tears would be shed because of this. But the crow said, "Caw, caw," and that all would pass off peaceably.

It was now determined that, on this fine morning, they should at once begin to ascend, so that hereafter no one should be able to say, "I could easily have flown much higher, but the evening came on, and I could do no more."

On a given signal, therefore, the whole troop rose up in the air. The dust ascended from the land, and there was tremendous fluttering and whirring and beating of wings. It looked as if a black cloud was rising up. The little birds were, however, soon left behind. They could go no farther, and fell back to the ground.

The larger birds held out longer, but none could equal the eagle, who mounted so high that he could have picked the eyes out of the sun. And when he saw that the others could not get up to him, he thought, "Why should I fly any higher, I am the King?" and began to let himself down again.

The birds beneath him at once cried to him, "You must be our King, no one has flown so high as you."

"Except me," screamed the little fellow without a name, who had crept into the breast-feathers of the eagle. And as he was not at all tired, he rose up and mounted so high that he reached heaven itself. When, however, he had gone as far as this, he folded his wings together, and called down with clear and penetrating voice:

"I am King! I am King!"

"You, our King?" cried the birds angrily. "You have done this by trick and cunning!"

Many stories incorporate a lesson or some kind of advice into them. What lesson can you take away from this story?

69

Exercises

1. What do the birds plan to choose?

   A. a new nest
   B. a queen
   C. a new country
   D. a king

CCSS.ELA-LITERACY.RL.3.1

4. Which of the following words can replace the word ascend in the story?

   A. climb
   B. leave
   C. spin
   D. fall

CCSS.ELA-LITERACY.RL.3.4

2. Where does the green plover go?

   A. to a new nest
   B. to a new country
   C. to a marsh
   D. to a cave in the mountains

CCSS.ELA-LITERACY.RL.3.3

5. What do the birds do to help decide upon a king

CCSS.ELA-LITERACY.RL.3.3

3. What does each the bird want to do?

   A. fly the fastest
   B. fly the farthest
   C. fly the highest
   D. fly for the longest time

CCSS.ELA-LITERACY.RL.3.1

6. Which bird do you predict might become King and why?

CCSS.ELA-LITERACY.RL.3.3

WEEK 8

VIDEO
EXPLANATIONS

ARGOPREP.COM

Find detailed video explanations to each problem on:
ArgoPrep.com or Download our app: **ArgoPrep Video Explanations**

Pronouns

CCSS.ELA-LITERACY.L.3.1.F

A pronoun takes the place of a noun. A pronoun must match the noun it is referring to.

Here are some examples:

Liv packed a sandwich.

She packed a sandwich.

The pronoun is she. She refers to Liv.

The sisters packed.

They packed.

The pronoun is they. They refers to the sisters.

The library changed the policy.

It changed the policy.

The pronoun is it. It refers to the library.

Pronouns are used to replace nouns in sentences.

Let's practice!

When using pronouns in your conversations or writing, be sure to identify that person or thing first that the pronoun refers to.

Exercises

Read the sentences. Rewrite each one with a pronoun.

1. Sarah loves to read.

CCSS.ELA-LITERACY.L.3.1.F

4. The cats ran under the deck.

CCSS.ELA-LITERACY.L.3.1.F

2. Joey and John live in Alabama.

CCSS.ELA-LITERACY.L.3.1.F

5. The baby was crying before her nap.

CCSS.ELA-LITERACY.L.3.1.F

3. The children misbehaved during recess.

CCSS.ELA-LITERACY.L.3.1.F

6. Mrs. Wilson was absent from school.

CCSS.ELA-LITERACY.L.3.1.F

Find detailed video explanations to each problem on:
ArgoPrep.com or Download our app: **ArgoPrep Video Explanations**

Pronouns and Antecedents

CCSS.ELA-LITERACY.L.3.1.F

A pronoun takes the place of a noun. An antecedent is the word that it refers back to.

Here are some examples:

Liv packed a sandwich for her lunch.

The pronoun is her.
The antecedent is Liv.
Her refers to Liv.

The sisters packed their suitcases.
The pronoun is their.
The antecedent is sisters.
Their refers to the sisters.

The library changed its policy about checking out books.
The pronoun is its.
The antecedent is library.
Its refers to library.

Let's practice!

TIP of the DAY

Pronouns are helpful for long paragraphs and conversations. After referring to the noun by name, use an appropriate pronoun 1-3 times in the sentences that follow. Then use the noun again every few sentences. This keeps your writing clear and makes sure that your reader stays on track with understanding your ideas.

Exercises

Read the sentences. Complete each one with the correct pronoun.

1. We decided to meet at one o'clock for _____ game.

   CCSS.ELA-LITERACY.L.3.1.F

2. The man went to the store before _____ meeting.

   CCSS.ELA-LITERACY.L.3.1.F

3. He presented _____ science project to the class.

   CCSS.ELA-LITERACY.L.3.1.F

4. Miriam lives in the neighborhood near _____ cousins.

   CCSS.ELA-LITERACY.L.3.1.F

5. The book was interesting to Natalie, and kept _____ reading for hours.

   CCSS.ELA-LITERACY.L.3.1.F

6. Strawberries wear seeds on _____ outsides.

   CCSS.ELA-LITERACY.L.3.1.F

Find detailed video explanations to each problem on:
ArgoPrep.com or Download our app: **ArgoPrep Video Explanations**

Pronoun Agreement

CCSS.ELA-LITERACY.L.3.1.F

A pronoun takes the place of a noun. An antecedent is the word that it refers back to.

The antecedent must agree in both gender and number.

Look at the examples below:

Jessica fixed her locker. (Jessica and her are both feminine and singular.)

Brayden called his friend. (Brayden and his are both masculine and singular.)

The boys completed their studying. (The plural pronoun agrees with the plural antecedent.)

The girls read magazines in their free time. (The plural pronoun agrees with the plural antecedent.)

Pronouns are used to replace nouns. They must agree in gender and number.

Let's practice!

To practice pronouns, write down a list of ten different specific nouns. Include objects, places, and people. Then write as many pronouns under each one that might be used in your writing. Make sure the pronoun matches the noun in gender and number.

Exercises

Circle the pronoun in the sentence. Then write S on the line for singular, or P on the line for plural.

1. The teacher asked the students to take their seats.

CCSS.ELA-LITERACY.L.3.1.F

4. Mrs. Denton lives with her sister.

CCSS.ELA-LITERACY.L.3.1.F

2. The girl practiced her ballet skills.

CCSS.ELA-LITERACY.L.3.1.F

5. I went to the museum last week.

CCSS.ELA-LITERACY.L.3.1.F

3. The dogs chased their tails.

CCSS.ELA-LITERACY.L.3.1.F

6. Blake loves to listen to his music before a game.

CCSS.ELA-LITERACY.L.3.1.F

WEEK 9

VIDEO
EXPLANATIONS

ARGOPREP.COM

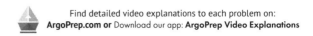

Excerpt from **The Cousin from Boston**

We had been friends ever since I could remember, Nelly and I. We were just about the same age. Our parents were neighbors, in the quiet country town where we both lived. I was an only child; and Nelly was an only daughter, with two strong brothers who idolized her.

We were always together. We went to the same school, and sat on the same bench, and used the same desk. We learned the same lessons. I had almost said we thought the same thoughts. We certainly loved the same pleasures. We used to go together, in early spring, to hunt the dainty may-flowers from under the sheltering dead leaves, and to find the shy little blue-eyed violets. We went hand in hand into the still summer woods, and gathered the delicate maiden-hair, and the soft mosses, and all the summer wealth of bud and blossom. Little birds sang to us. The deep blue sky bent over us, and the happy little brooks murmured and frolicked at our feet.

In autumn we went nutting and apple gathering. In the winter we slid, and coasted, and snowballed. For every season, there was some special pleasure, — and always Nelly and I were together, — always sufficient to each other, for company. We never dreamed that any thing could come between us, or that we could ever learn to live without each other.

We were thirteen when Nelly's cousin from Boston — Lill Simmonds, her name was — came to see her. It was vacation then, and I had not seen Nelly for two days, because it had been raining hard. So I did not know of the expected guest, until one morning Nelly's brother Tom came over, and told me that his Aunt Simmonds, from Boston, was expected that noon, and with her his Cousin Lill.

"She'll be a nice playmate for you and Nelly," he said. "She's only a year older than you two, and she used to have plenty of fun in her. Nelly wants you to come over this afternoon, sure."

That was the beginning of my feeling hard toward Nelly. I was unreasonable, I know, but I thought she might have come to tell me the news, herself. I felt a sort of bitter, shut-out feeling all the forenoon, and after dinner I was half minded not to go over, — to let her have her Boston cousin all to herself.

My mother heard some of my speeches, but she was wise enough not to interfere. When she saw, at last, that curiosity and inclination had gotten the better of pique and jealousy, she basted a fresh ruffle in the neck of my afternoon dress, and tied a pretty blue ribbon in my hair, and I looked as neat and suitable for the occasion as possible.

At least I thought so, until I got to Nelly's. She did not watch for my coming, and run to the gate to meet me, as usual. Of course it was perfectly natural that she should be entertaining her cousin, but I missed the accustomed greeting; and when she heard my voice at the door, and came out of the parlor to speak to me, I know that if my face reflected my heart, it must have worn a most sullen and unamiable expression.

"I'm so glad you've come, Sophie," she said cheerfully. "Lill is in the parlor. I want you to like her. But you can't help it, I know, she's so lovely; such a beauty."

How does the author use setting in this story? Why is understanding the setting so important?

"Perhaps I shan't see with your eyes," I answered, with what I imagined to be most cutting coldness and dignity.

"Oh yes! I guess you will," she laughed. "We have thought alike about most things, all our lives."

I followed her into the parlor, and I saw Lill. If you are a country girl who read, and have ever been suddenly confronted with a city young lady in the height of fashion, to whom you were expected to make yourself agreeable, you can, perhaps, understand what I felt; particularly if by nature you are not only sensitive, but somewhat vain, as I am sorry to confess I was. I had been used to think myself as well-dressed, and as well-looking as any of my young neighbors; I was neither as well-dressed nor as well-looking as Lill Simmonds.

Nelly was right. She was a beauty. She was a little taller than Nelly or I, — a slender, graceful creature, with a high-bred air. It was years before they had begun to crimp little girls' hair, but I think Lill's must have been crimped. It was a perfect golden cloud about her face and shoulders, and all full of little shining waves and ripples. Then what eyes she had — star bright and deep blue and with lashes so long that when they drooped they cast a shadow on the pale pink of her cheeks. Her features were all delicate and pure; her hands white, with one or two glittering rings upon them; and her clothes! My own gowns had not seemed to me ill-made before; but now I thought Nelly and I both looked as if we had come out of the ark. It was the first of September, and her dress had just been made for fall, — a rich, glossy, blue poplin, with soft lace at throat and wrists, and a pin and some tiny ear jewels of exquisitely cut pink coral.

Exercises

1. Where does this story take place?

   A. in the mountains
   B. in Boston
   C. in the country
   D. near the ocean

   CCSS.ELA-LITERACY.RL.3.1

4. Who is the narrator of the story?

   A. Lill
   B. Sophie
   C. Nelly
   D. Tom

   CCSS.ELA-LITERACY.RL.3.1

2. Which of the following words can replace *frolicked* in the story?

   A. swam
   B. ran
   C. jumped
   D. played

   CCSS.ELA-LITERACY.RL.3.4

5. What does the word *sullen* mean?

   A. gloomy
   B. scared
   C. tired
   D. confused

   CCSS.ELA-LITERACY.RL.3.4

3. Who is Lill?

   A. Nelly's cousin
   B. Nelly's sister
   C. Sophie's cousin
   D. Sophie's sister

   CCSS.ELA-LITERACY.RL.3.3

6. Which adjective describes Lill?

   A. tiny
   B. shy
   C. exquisite
   D. old

   CCSS.ELA-LITERACY.RL.3.4

Find detailed video explanations to each problem on:
ArgoPrep.com or Download our app: **ArgoPrep Video Explanations**

Excerpt from **Thin Ice**

The little village of Westbrook seemed to have been standing still, while all the rest of the world had gone on. The people lived very much as their fathers and grandfathers had lived before them. They were all farmers except the doctor and the minister.

The doctor was a very skilful man; but he had been reared on a Westbrook farm, and when he went out into the world to get his medical education he had brought back with him, to quiet Westbrook, only the knowledge he sought, and none of the airs and graces of town life.

The minister, too, was Westbrook born and bred, and his wife had scarcely ever been outside the town in all her days, so that there was no one in the simple community to set extravagant fashions, or turn foolish heads by splendor.

It was, therefore, as much of an event as if Queen Victoria herself were to come and spend the winter in Boston, when it became generally known that a rich widow lady and her son were to come, the last of September, and very probably stay on through the winter under Dr. Simms's roof. A famous city physician, with whom Dr. Simms had studied once, had recommended him and Westbrook to Mrs. Rosenburgh, when it became necessary for her to take her puny boy into some still, country retreat.

They came during the last golden days of September, and all Westbrook was alive with interest about them. The lady looked delicate, but she was as pretty as she was pale, and her boy was curiously like her, — as pale, as pretty, almost as feminine.

There was plenty of opportunity to see them, for the city doctor had given orders that the young gentleman should keep out of doors all the time; so, mornings, he and his mother were always to be seen in their low, luxurious carriage, drawn by high-stepping bay horses, and driven by a faithful, careful, middle-aged man, with iron-gray hair and an impenetrable face.

Sometimes, in the afternoons, they would all be out again, but oftener Mrs. Rosenburgh remained at home, and her son drove, for himself, a pair of pretty black ponies, while the impenetrable, iron-gray man sat behind, ready to seize the reins in case of accident.

At first the boy's face seemed often drawn by pain, or white with weariness, and he would look round him listlessly, as he drove, with eyes that saw nothing, or at least failed to find any object of interest. But the clear autumn air proved invigorating, and when the glorious, prismatic days of late October came he looked as if, indeed, he had been re-created.

And now one could see that he began to take a natural, human interest in what went on around him. He would drive up his little pony carriage to the wall, and look over it to watch the apple-pickers and the harvesters. No one spoke to him, and he spoke to no one. The lads of his own age, who watched his ponies with boyish envy, never dreamed that the owner of these fairy coursers could be as shy as one of themselves, and, indeed, as much more shy as delicate weakness naturally is than rosy strength. They thought his silence was pride, and felt a half-defiant hatred of him accordingly.

TIP of the **DAY**

The last sentence of this excerpt utilizes foreshadowing. Foreshadowing gives clues about what might occur later in a story. What might the last sentence predict?

Yet many and many a day he went home to his mother, and sitting beside her with his head upon her knee, cried out, in very bitterness, —

"Oh if I only could be like one of those healthy boys! How gladly I'd give up Pease-blossom and Mustard-seed, to be able to run about as they do! Shall I never, never be strong, mamma?"

And she would comfort him with the happy truth that every day he was growing stronger, and that she expected him to be her great, brave boy, by and by, who would take care of her all the days of her life.

Meantime, other boys, in other homes, talked to other mothers. For the very first time the evil spirit of envy had crept into quiet Westbrook.

Exercises

1. What do most of the people in Westbrook do for a living?

   A. They are ministers.
   B. They are doctors.
   C. They are blacksmiths.
   D. They are farmers.

4. Which of the following words can replace the word *puny* in the story?

   A. wise
   B. short
   C. scrawny
   D. bold

2. Which of the following can replace the word *extravagant* in the story?

   A. embellished
   B. moderate
   C. plain
   D. unknown

5. What does the boy hope for?

   A. new friends
   B. strength
   C. more money
   D. a new pony

3. Why does Mrs. Rosenburgh and her son come to Westbrook?

   A. to visit family
   B. to take a vacation
   C. to attend a new place of worship
   D. to take care of the boy's health

6. What does the word *envy* mean?

   A. grudge
   B. kindness
   C. jealousy
   D. faith

Find detailed video explanations to each problem on:
ArgoPrep.com or Download our app: **ArgoPrep Video Explanations**

October's Bright Blue Weather
Helen Hunt Jackson

O suns and skies and clouds of June,
  And flowers of June together,
Ye cannot rival for one hour
  October's bright blue weather;

When loud the bumblebee makes haste,
  Belated, thriftless vagrant,
And goldenrod is dying fast,
  And lanes with grapes are fragrant;

When gentians roll their fringes tight
  To save them for the morning,
And chestnuts fall from satin burrs
  Without a sound of warning;

When on the ground red apples lie
  In piles like jewels shining,
And redder still on old stone walls
  Are leaves of woodbine twining;

When all the lovely wayside things
  Their white-winged seeds are sowing,
And in the fields, still green and fair,
  Late aftermaths are growing;

When springs run low, and on the brooks,
  In idle, golden freighting,
Bright leaves sink noiseless in the hush
  Of woods, for winter waiting;

When comrades seek sweet country haunts,
  By twos and threes together,
And count like misers hour by hour,
  October's bright blue weather.

O suns and skies and flowers of June,
  Count all your boasts together,
Love loveth best of all the year
  October's bright blue weather.

TIP of the DAY

A group of thoughts in a poem is known as a stanza. A stanza is similar to a paragraph in an essay or story.

Exercises

1. Which word is a synonym for the word *rival*?

   A. cry
   B. scream
   C. steal
   D. match

   CCSS.ELA-LITERACY.RL.3.4

4. Which word can replace the word *comrades* in the story?

   A. foes
   B. enemies
   C. visitors
   D. friends

   CCSS.ELA-LITERACY.RL.3.4

2. What does the author compare apples to?

   A. jewels
   B. peaches
   C. dessert
   D. softballs

   CCSS.ELA-LITERACY.RL.3.1

5. What reasons does the author give to support her opinion that October is a great month?

   CCSS.ELA-LITERACY.RL.3.1

3. Which month does the author make a comparison to?

   A. July
   B. August
   C. June
   D. September

   CCSS.ELA-LITERACY.RL.3.1

6. What things do you do in October that are similar to what is mentioned in the poem? Share specific examples.

   CCSS.ELA-LITERACY.RL.3.2

WEEK 10

VIDEO
EXPLANATIONS

ARGOPREP.COM

Find detailed video explanations to each problem on:
ArgoPrep.com or Download our app: **ArgoPrep Video Explanations**

Adjectives

CCSS.ELA-LITERACY.L.3.1.G

An adjective is a word that describes a noun. It tells what kind. It can also tell how many.

Look at the examples below:

What Kind:

They live in a new house.

The children rode their blue bikes.

Matthew painted a colorful picture.

The adjectives new, blue, and colorful all tell what kind.

How Many:

There are four roses in the vase.

The family has five children.

The doctor has worked in this hospital for thirteen years.

The adjectives four, five, and thirteen all tell how many.

Adjectives are describing words.

Let's practice!

Adjectives add to the quality of a sentence. For each noun you include in a sentence, aim to include at least one adjective that describes it.

Exercises

Read the sentences. Circle the adjective in each sentence.

1. She lives in the yellow house on the corner.

CCSS.ELA-LITERACY.L.3.1.G

4. Thomas ate four cookies.

CCSS.ELA-LITERACY.L.3.1.G

2. John walked to school in his blue shoes.

CCSS.ELA-LITERACY.L.3.1.G

5. Hal ran for one hour.

CCSS.ELA-LITERACY.L.3.1.G

3. Melissa sings with her pretty voice.

CCSS.ELA-LITERACY.L.3.1.G

6. The rabbits went into the small burrow.

CCSS.ELA-LITERACY.L.3.1.G

Week 10 - Wednesday

Find detailed video explanations to each problem on:
ArgoPrep.com or Download our app: **ArgoPrep Video Explanations**

Comparative Adjectives

CCSS.ELA-LITERACY.L.3.1.G

Adjectives are describing words. Sometimes adjectives compare two things to one another. These are known as comparative adjectives.

You can add −er to an adjective to compare two things.

Here are some examples:

Rachel is faster than Julie.

Jill's brother is taller than her.

The worm was slower than the grasshopper.

My sandcastle is taller than yours.

Jeremy's car is cleaner than mine.

When you want to describe while comparing two things, you must use a comparative adjective.

Let's practice!

TIP of the DAY

Think of ways you can compare two or more objects in your classroom. What adjectives can describe them in a comparative manner?

Exercises

Complete the sentence with a comparative adjective.

1. I am _____ than John at school.

CCSS.ELA-LITERACY.L.3.1.G

2. Joshua is _____ than Jennifer.

CCSS.ELA-LITERACY.L.3.1.G

3. Drew is _____ than Jake during practice.

CCSS.ELA-LITERACY.L.3.1.G

Write a sentence on each line using the given comparative adjective.

4. brighter

CCSS.ELA-LITERACY.L.3.1.G

5. faster

CCSS.ELA-LITERACY.L.3.1.G

6. lower

CCSS.ELA-LITERACY.L.3.1.G

Week 10 - Friday

Find detailed video explanations to each problem on:
ArgoPrep.com or Download our app: **ArgoPrep Video Explanations**

Superlative Adjectives

CCSS.ELA-LITERACY.L.3.1.G

Adjectives are describing words. Sometimes adjectives compare three or more things to one another. These are known as superlative adjectives.

You can add –est to an adjective to compare three or more things.

Here are some examples:

Rachel is the fastest in the class.

Jill's brother is the tallest person in their family.

The worm is the slowest of their science habitat.

My sandcastle is the tallest on the beach.

Jeremy's car is the cleanest in the parking lot.

When you want to describe while comparing three or more things, you must use a superlative adjective.

Let's practice!

TIP of the **DAY**

Think of ways you can compare three or more objects in your classroom. What adjectives can describe them in a comparative manner?

Exercises

Complete the sentence with a superlative adjective.

1. He is the _____ in the school.

CCSS.ELA-LITERACY.L.3.1.G

2. James is the _____ boy on the swim team.

CCSS.ELA-LITERACY.L.3.1.G

3. Gina is the _____ when cleaning up the art supplies.

CCSS.ELA-LITERACY.L.3.1.G

Write a sentence on each line using the given superlative adjective.

4. shortest

CCSS.ELA-LITERACY.L.3.1.G

5. quietest

CCSS.ELA-LITERACY.L.3.1.G

6. biggest

CCSS.ELA-LITERACY.L.3.1.G

WEEK 11

VIDEO
EXPLANATIONS

ARGOPREP.COM

 Find detailed video explanations to each problem on:
ArgoPrep.com or Download our app: **ArgoPrep Video Explanations**

The Fox and the Goat

A Fox one day fell into a deep well and could find no means of escape. A Goat, overcome with thirst, came to the same well, and seeing the Fox, inquired if the water was good.

Concealing his sad plight under a merry guise, the Fox indulged in a lavish praise of the water, saying it was excellent beyond measure, and encouraging him to descend. The Goat, mindful only of his thirst, thoughtlessly jumped down, but just as he drank, the Fox informed him of the difficulty they were both in and suggested a scheme for their common escape.

"If," said he, "you will place your forefeet upon the wall and bend your head, I will run up your back and escape, and will help you out afterwards."

The Goat readily assented and the Fox leaped upon his back. Steadying himself with the Goat's horns, he safely reached the mouth of the well and made off as fast as he could. When the Goat upbraided him for breaking his promise, he turned around and cried out, "You foolish old fellow! If you had as many brains in your head as you have hairs in your beard, you would never have gone down before you had inspected the way up, nor have exposed yourself to dangers from which you had no means of escape."

Look before you leap.

What does "Look before you leap" mean? How can you apply this advice to your own actions?

Exercises

1. Where is the Fox at the beginning of the story?

   A. in a cave
   B. in a burrow
   C. in a well
   D. in the sea

4. Which word best describes the Goat's decision to join the Fox?

   A. smart
   B. hasty
   C. selfless
   D. funny

2. What is the Goat focused on?

   A. eating the Fox
   B. his thirst
   C. resting
   D. getting home

5. What does the Fox promise?

   A. money
   B. food
   C. water
   D. help

3. What is another word for *encouraging* in the story?

   A. convincing
   B. smiling
   C. greeting
   D. relying

6. Which word best describes the Goat?

   A. foolish
   B. kind
   C. strong
   D. loud

The Thief and the Innkeeper

A Thief hired a room in a tavern and stayed a while in the hope of stealing something, which should enable him to pay his reckoning. When he had waited some days in vain, he saw the Innkeeper dressed in a new and handsome coat and sitting before his door.

The Thief sat down beside him and talked with him. As the conversation began to flag, the Thief yawned terribly and at the same time howled like a wolf.

The Innkeeper said, "Why do you howl so fearfully?"

"I will tell you," said the Thief, "but first let me ask you to hold my clothes, or I shall tear them to pieces. I know not, sir, when I got this habit of yawning, nor whether these attacks of howling were inflicted on me as a judgment for my crimes, or for any other cause; but this I do know, that when I yawn for the third time, I actually turn into a wolf and attack men."

With this speech he commenced a second fit of yawning and again howled like a wolf, as he had at first. The Innkeeper, hearing his tale and believing what he said, became greatly alarmed and, rising from his seat, attempted to run away.

The Thief laid hold of his coat and entreated him to stop, saying, "Pray wait, sir, and hold my clothes, or I shall tear them to pieces in my fury, when I turn into a wolf."

At the same moment he yawned the third time and set up a terrible howl. The Innkeeper, frightened lest he should be attacked, left his new coat in the Thief's hand and ran as fast as he could into the inn for safety. The Thief made off with the coat and did not return again to the inn.

Every tale is not to be believed.

TIP of the DAY

Comparing two characters to one another can be a helpful way to learn about them. Divide a piece of paper in half. One half will be used for the Thief and the other half will be used for the Innkeeper. What adjectives and actions can you write on each side? Contrast the two characters.

Exercises

1. Where does the story take place?

   A. a diner
   B. a home
   C. a tavern
   D. a butcher shop

   CCSS.ELA-LITERACY.RL.3.1

4. What does the Innkeeper do?

   A. He tries to run away.
   B. He puts the Thief in a cage.
   C. He calls the police.
   D. He laughs.

   CCSS.ELA-LITERACY.RL.3.3

2. What is the job of an innkeeper?

   A. to cook food
   B. to do the laundry
   C. to deliver packages
   D. to take care of the hotel

   CCSS.ELA-LITERACY.RL.3.4

5. Which word describes the Innkeeper?

   A. intelligent
   B. sassy
   C. gullible
   D. overworked

   CCSS.ELA-LITERACY.RL.3.4

3. What is the reason the Thief says he howls?

   A. He is trying to become a wolf.
   B. He has been punished.
   C. He is taking acting classes.
   D. He did not learn how to speak.

   CCSS.ELA-LITERACY.RL.3.3

6. What lesson can be learned from the story?

   A. Kindness matters.
   B. Honesty is the best policy.
   C. Try try again.
   D. Don't believe everything.

   CCSS.ELA-LITERACY.RL.3.3

Find detailed video explanations to each problem on:
 ArgoPrep.com or Download our app: **ArgoPrep Video Explanations**

The Lark and Her Young Ones

A Lark had made her nest in the early spring on the young green wheat.

The brood had almost grown to their full strength and attained the use of their wings and the full plumage of their feathers, when the owner of the field, looking over his ripe crop, said, "The time has come when I must ask all my neighbors to help me with my harvest."

One of the young Larks heard his speech and related it to his mother, inquiring of her to what place they should move for safety. "There is no occasion to move yet, my son," she replied; "the man who only sends to his friends to help him with his harvest is not really in earnest."

The owner of the field came again a few days later and saw the wheat shedding the grain from excess of ripeness. He said, "I will come myself tomorrow with my laborers, and with as many reapers as I can hire, and will get in the harvest."

The Lark on hearing these words said to her brood, "It is time now to be off, my little ones, for the man is in earnest this time; he no longer trusts his friends, but will reap the field himself."

Self-help is the best help.

Fables teach a lesson, and are often sort in length. However, short texts can still provide a lot of information.

Exercises

1. What is a Lark?

   A. a squirrel
   B. a bird
   C. a mole
   D. a butterfly

CCSS.ELA-LITERACY.RL.2.1

4. What is the job of a reaper?

   A. to clean
   B. to build
   C. to deliver
   D. to farm

CCSS.ELA-LITERACY.RL.3.4

2. Which of the following is a synonym for the word *brood* in the story?

   A. offspring
   B. friend
   C. prey
   D. foe

CCSS.ELA-LITERACY.RL.3.4

5. What does the Lark tell her brood at the end of the story?

CCSS.ELA-LITERACY.RL.3.3

3. Which word can replace the word *harvest* in the story?

   A. home
   B. money
   C. gathering
   D. family

CCSS.ELA-LITERACY.RL.3.4

6. What lesson can be learned from this story?

CCSS.ELA-LITERACY.RL.3.2

WEEK 12

VIDEO
EXPLANATIONS

Commas in Writing

CCSS.ELA-LITERACY.L.3.2.C

A comma is used to separate groups of three or more words. Three or more nouns or adjectives in a row are known as items in a series. By using commas, the information becomes more clear to the reader.

Here are some examples:

Julia ran past the pond, park bench, and gazebo yesterday.

The commas separate the three places she ran past.

Children in the class colored with red, yellow, blue, and green crayons.

The commas in this series help to separate the four colors: red, yellow, blue, and green.

Bob, Jake, Ted, and Mark played golf on Sunday.

The commas in the series are used to separate the four names: Bob, Jake, Ted, and Mark.

Jennifer is kind, smart, and friendly.

The commas in this series separate three adjectives: kind, smart, and friendly.

Commas are used in a series to make information clear.

Let's practice!

Commas are often located in the places we pause when speaking or reading a sentence.

102

Exercises

Read each sentence. Add commas where they belong. If commas are not needed, write none on the line.

1. Lila Debbie and Joan were in the same book club together.

4. Elizabeth loves going to the movies ice skating and shopping with her friends.

2. Madison has lived in Texas New York Minnesota and Idaho.

5. Derek Timothy Rich Joe and Justin are on the same team.

3. The dogs played with the ball and the sticks.

6. Hannah Elizabeth and Mariah Rose played tag and hopscotch after school.

Find detailed video explanations to each problem on:
ArgoPrep.com or Download our app: **ArgoPrep Video Explanations**

Commas in Addresses and Dates

CCSS.ELA-LITERACY.L.3.2.C

Commas are also used In addresses to separate the street address, city, and state.

This makes the information about a specific location clear to the reader.

For example:

Lisa lives at 381 Huckleberry Street, Walton, New Jersey.

I am travelling to Las Vegas, Nevada next week.

The family moved from Houston, Texas to Orlando, Florida last year.

Sherri is interested in buying the property at 190 East Avenue, Brighton, Tennessee.

Commas are also used in dates.

See the examples below:

July 10, 2015

October 29, 1995

March 2, 1873

August 15, 2024

Using commas in addresses to separate the street address and the city and state is helpful in conveying clear information.

Using commas in dates before the year provides clear information as well.

Let's practice!

Practice writing a postcard or addressing an envelope to a friend or relative. Be sure to include commas where needed.

Exercises

Add commas where needed in the sentences below.

1. Lisa lives in Los Angeles California.

4. The foreign language students will go on a trip to Paris France on May 23 2020.

2. The city of Albuquerque New Mexico is a beautiful place to explore.

5. We will soon move to 9845 West Dover Street in Middleton Delaware.

3. The diner is located at 439 Little Lane West Newton Ohio.

6. Georgia visited her aunt on July 18 2019 in Raleigh North Carolina.

Week 12 - Friday

Find detailed video explanations to each problem on:
ArgoPrep.com or Download our app: **ArgoPrep Video Explanations**

Commas in Dialogue

CCSS.ELA-LITERACY.L.3.2.C

When you use a comma in your writing, it is similar to pausing when you speak.

When writing dialogue, or conversation, a comma is used to set off the speaker from what he or she is saying.

Here are some examples:

Susan said, "I'd love to go to the movies today!"

Mark shared, "This is my best piece of artwork."

Tim stated, "The rules are the same for everyone."

Dr. Thompson advised, "Be sure to get plenty of rest so you will feel better soon."

Commas have many uses including separating items in a series, in addresses, in dates, and within dialogue.

Let's practice!

Using a comma in dialogue lets the reader know that direct text is being stated next.

Exercises

Rewrite each sentence, adding commas as needed to clarify the dialogue.

1. Tony told Sammi "I will be back by seven o'clock."

4. John told the doctor "I have had a headache for three days now."

2. Delaney, Josh, and Sarah all chanted "Go, team, go!"

5. After leaving for her trip, Caroline called her mom and told her "My flight will land at nine thirty tonight."

3. After visiting her aunt, Myra thanked her and said "See you soon!"

6. Before going to school, Jeff's mom asked him "Did you remember to get your lunchbox?"

WEEK 13

VIDEO
EXPLANATIONS

ARGOPREP.COM

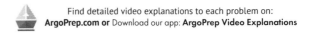

The Town Mouse and the Country Mouse

A Country Mouse invited a Town Mouse, an intimate friend, to pay him a visit and partake of his country fare.

As they were on the bare plowlands, eating there wheat-stocks and roots pulled up from the hedgerow, the Town Mouse said to his friend, "You live here the life of the ants, while in my house is the horn of plenty. I am surrounded by every luxury, and if you will come with me, as I wish you would, you shall have an ample share of my dainties."

The Country Mouse was easily persuaded, and returned to town with his friend. On his arrival, the Town Mouse placed before him bread, barley, beans, dried figs, honey, raisins, and, last of all, brought a dainty piece of cheese from a basket.

The Country Mouse, being much delighted at the sight of such good cheer, expressed his satisfaction in warm terms and lamented his own hard fate. Just as they were beginning to eat, someone opened the door, and they both ran off squeaking, as fast as they could, to a hole so narrow that two could only find room in it by squeezing. They had scarcely begun their repast again when someone else entered to take something out of a cupboard, whereupon the two Mice, more frightened than before, ran away and hid themselves.

At last the Country Mouse, almost famished, said to his friend: "Although you have prepared for me so dainty a feast, I must leave you to enjoy it by yourself. It is surrounded by too many dangers to please me. I prefer my bare plowlands and roots from the hedgerow, where I can live in safety, and without fear."

Were you familiar with this well-known tale before reading it? How can familiarity help with reading new stories?

Exercises

1. Where does the Town Mouse go?

   A. to visit his friend
   B. to the market
   C. to work
   D. to hibernate

   CCSS.ELA-LITERACY.RL.3.1

4. What makes the Country Mouse so happy?

   A. the sunshine
   B. the food
   C. good company
   D. money

   CCSS.ELA-LITERACY.RL.3.3

2. Where does the Town Mouse then want to go?

   A. to the countryside
   B. to the city
   C. to the desert
   D. to the mountains

   CCSS.ELA-LITERACY.RL.3.1

5. Where do the mice run to?

   A. a hole
   B. the attic
   C. the shed
   D. a garage

   CCSS.ELA-LITERACY.RL.3.1

3. Which of the following words is a synonym for *persuaded*?

   A. loved
   B. helped
   C. tricked
   D. convinced

   CCSS.ELA-LITERACY.RL.3.4

6. Why does the Country Mouse leave?

   A. It is too hot.
   B. It is too rainy.
   C. It is too far away.
   D. It is too dangerous.

   CCSS.ELA-LITERACY.RL.3.2

The Peasant and the Apple Tree

A peasant had in his garden an apple tree, which bore no fruit but only served as a harbor for the sparrows and grasshoppers. He resolved to cut it down, and taking his axe in his hand, made a bold stroke at its roots.

The grasshoppers and sparrows entreated him not to cut down the tree that sheltered them, but to spare it, and they would sing to him and lighten his labors. He paid no attention to their request, but gave the tree a second and a third blow with his axe.

When he reached the hollow of the tree, he found a hive full of honey. Having tasted the honeycomb, he threw down his axe, and looking on the tree as sacred, took great care of it.

Self-interest alone moves some men.

How might this story be expanded? If you were the author, how could you add more information to it? Practice your writing skills by extending the plot of the story.

Exercises

1. What kind of fruit does the tree have?

   A. apples
   B. oranges
   C. pears
   D. none

CCSS.ELA-LITERACY.RL.3.1

4. Which word can replace the word *sheltered* in the story?

   A. protected
   B. helped
   C. left
   D. housed

CCSS.ELA-LITERACY.RL.3.4

2. What does the peasant want to do to the tree?

   A. Climb it
   B. Put a swing in it
   C. Chop it down
   D. Eat fruit from it

CCSS.ELA-LITERACY.RL.3.1

5. Where is the hollow of a tree located?

   A. in the trunk
   B. on the smallest branches
   C. in the roots
   D. on the leaves

CCSS.ELA-LITERACY.RL.3.4

3. Which word describes the peasant?

   A. lazy
   B. selfish
   C. old
   D. kind

CCSS.ELA-LITERACY.RL.3.4

6. What does the peasant find?

   A. baby birds
   B. more apples
   C. honey
   D. bees

CCSS.ELA-LITERACY.RL.3.3

Find detailed video explanations to each problem on:
ArgoPrep.com or Download our app: **ArgoPrep Video Explanations**

The Lion, Jupiter, and the Elephant

The Lion wearied Jupiter with his frequent complaints. "It is true, O Jupiter!" he said, "that I am gigantic in strength, handsome in shape, and powerful in attack. I have jaws well provided with teeth, and feet furnished with claws, and I lord it over all the beasts of the forest, and what a disgrace it is, that being such as I am, I should be frightened by the crowing of a rooster."

Jupiter replied, "Why do you blame me without a cause? I have given you all the attributes which I possess myself, and your courage never fails you except in this one instance."

On hearing this the Lion groaned and lamented very much and, reproaching himself with his cowardice, wished that he might die. As these thoughts passed through his mind, he met an Elephant and came close to hold a conversation with him. After a time he observed that the Elephant shook his ears very often, and he inquired what was the matter and why his ears moved with such a tremor every now and then.

Just at that moment a Gnat settled on the head of the Elephant, and he replied, "Do you see that little buzzing insect? If it enters my ear, my fate is sealed. I should die presently."

The Lion said, "Well, since so huge a beast is afraid of a tiny gnat, I will no more complain, nor wish myself dead. I find myself, even as I am, better off than the Elephant."

In many stories, gods (like Jupiter) are included as a key part. How does this add an interesting element to the story?

Exercises

1. What does the Lion think of himself?

   A. He is strong.
   B. He is smart.
   C. He is brave.
   D. He is small.

4. What is a Gnat?

   A. a fish
   B. a germ
   C. an insect
   D. a particle of dust

2. Which word can replace the word *cowardice* in the story?

   A. bravery
   B. complexity
   C. eagerness
   D. timidity

5. What does the Lion notice about the Elephant?

   _____

   _____

   _____

   _____

3. Which of the following could replace the word *tremor* in the story?

   A. shake
   B. rush
   C. spill
   D. laughter

6. What lesson can be learned from this story?

   _____

   _____

   _____

   _____

WEEK 14

VIDEO
EXPLANATIONS

ARGOPREP.COM

Conjunctions

CCSS.ELA-LITERACY.L3.1.H

A conjunction is a word that connects two words, phrases, clauses, or sentences together.

Common conjunctions can be remembered by using the following acronym: FANBOYS

    for

    and

    nor

    but

    or

    yet

    so

Here are some examples:

My favorite colors are blue and yellow.

Would you like tea or coffee?

I'd go along with you, but I can't be late to work.

I like bananas and I eat one each day.

He wanted to join her, yet he was too scared to ask to tag along.

Conjunctions join information together.

Let's practice!

Memorizing the conjunctions using FANBOYS can be helpful as you practice your grammar skills and write stories and essays. Why are conjunctions an important part of our language?

Exercises

Complete the following by choosing the best conjunction that fits each sentence.

1. My mom (but / and) dad took me to the park.

4. Sarah does not like dance (but / or) softball.

2. John must study, (but / or) else he might not do well on the test.

5. The children were well-behaved (or / so) they earned a reward.

3. He wanted to join the club, (or / yet) he decided against it.

6. The dog loves treats (or / but) he does not love doing tricks for them.

Week 14 - Wednesday

Find detailed video explanations to each problem on:
ArgoPrep.com or Download our app: **ArgoPrep Video Explanations**

Coordinating Conjunctions

CCSS.ELA-LITERACY.L3.1.H

Coordinating conjunctions join two independent clauses to make a compound sentence.

Use a comma in between the first independent clause and the coordinating conjunction.

   Here are some examples:

   She has a lot of friends, and she was a kind person.

   I don't want to argue with you, but I don't think you are correct.

   James runs each morning, but on Fridays he swims instead.

   He studied for his test, and he got a good grade.

   You can choose an apple, or you can choose a pear.

Coordinating conjunctions join two independent thoughts together and include the words for, and, nor, but, or, yet, so.

Let's practice!

TIP of the **DAY**

Remember that coordinating conjunctions can be removed and replaced with an ending mark. This means that the two thoughts are independent and can stand alone. (If not, the conjunctions are not considered coordinating.)

Exercises

Combine the sentences with a comma and a coordinating conjunction.

1. I had that book. I lost it.

CCSS.ELA-LITERACY.L3.1.H

4. I can go to the store. I can go to the bank.

CCSS.ELA-LITERACY.L3.1.H

2. David moved to Florida. He moved home shortly after.

CCSS.ELA-LITERACY.L3.1.H

5. They didn't want to be late to school. They walked quickly.

CCSS.ELA-LITERACY.L3.1.H

3. Melissa can bake the cake. Theresa can cook the chicken.

CCSS.ELA-LITERACY.L3.1.H

6. The summer is my favorite time of the year. The spring time is nice too.

CCSS.ELA-LITERACY.L3.1.H

 Week 14 - Friday

Find detailed video explanations to each problem on:
ArgoPrep.com or Download our app: **ArgoPrep Video Explanations**

Subordinating Conjunctions

CCSS.ELA-LITERACY.L3.1.H

A subordinating conjunction connects an independent clause with a dependent clause. The dependent clause is followed with a comma.

Subordinating Conjunctions:

although	if	before
because	once	since
unless	whenever	while

Here are some examples:

Before you cook dinner, wash your hands.

I will wash your plate after you finish your dinner.

If you start working on your project, I will help you.

Subordinating conjunctions join a complete sentence with an incomplete sentence.

Let's practice!

Subordinating conjunctions join a complete thought with an incomplete thought. If the incomplete thought comes first in the sentence, it is followed by a comma.

Exercises

Choose a subordinating conjunction to complete each sentence.

1. It is surprising _____ you didn't join the chess club.

4. Greg felt proud _____ he earned a good grade.

2. I can't relax _____ I find my puppy.

5. The teacher read the rules _____ she started her lesson.

3. I am going to go inside her house _____ it's raining.

6. Erin couldn't go to school _____ she was sick.

WEEK 15

VIDEO
EXPLANATIONS

Find detailed video explanations to each problem on:
ArgoPrep.com or Download our app: **ArgoPrep Video Explanations**

The Frogs who asked for a King

There were once some Frogs who lived together in perfect security in a beautiful lake. They were a large company, and were very comfortable, but they came to think that they might be still happier if they had a King to rule over them.

So they sent to Jupiter, their god, to ask him to give them a King. Jupiter laughed at their folly, for he knew that they were better off as they were; but he said to them, "Well, here is a King for you," and into the water he threw a big Log.

It fell with such a splash that the Frogs were terrified and hid themselves in the deep mud under the water. By and by, one braver than the rest peeped out to look at the King, and saw the Log, as it lay quietly on the top of the water. Soon, one after another they all came out of their hiding places and ventured to look at their great King. As the Log did not move, they swam round it, keeping a safe distance away, and at last one by one hopped upon it.

"This is not a King," said a wise old Frog; "it is nothing but a stupid Log. If we had a King, Jupiter would pay more attention to us." Again they sent to Jupiter, and begged him to give them a King who could rule over them.

Jupiter did not like to be disturbed again by the silly Frogs, and this time he sent them a Stork, saying, "You will have some one to rule over you now." As they saw the Stork solemnly walking down to the lake, they were delighted.

"Ah!" they said, "see how grand he looks! How he strides along! How he throws back his head! This is a King indeed. He shall rule over us," and they went joyfully to meet him.

As their new King came nearer, he paused, stretched out his long neck, picked up the head Frog, and swallowed him at one mouthful. And then the next — and the next!

"What is this?" cried the Frogs, and they began to draw back in terror.

But the Stork with his long legs easily followed them to the water, and kept on eating them as fast as he could.

"Oh! If we had only been — " said the oldest Frog.

He was going to add "content," but was eaten up before he could finish the sentence.

The remaining Frogs cried to Jupiter to help them, but he would not listen. And the Stork-King ate them for breakfast, dinner, and supper, every day, till in a short time there was not a Frog left in the lake.

Poor foolish Frogs, not to have known when they were well off.

Why does the author refer to the frogs as being "foolish," and what lesson can you take away from this story?

Exercises

1. What did the Frogs think might make them happy?

   A. a larger pond
   B. more food
   C. a King
   D. a vacation

4. What word might describe the frogs?

   A. selfish
   B. wise
   C. foolish
   D. kind

2. Who do the Frogs seek help from?

   A. the moon
   B. Jupiter
   C. Saturn
   D. the sun

5. What is sent to the frogs?

   A. a stork
   B. a goose
   C. a god
   D. a fairy

3. What do the Frogs get?

   A. more lily pads
   B. a bigger pond
   C. a log
   D. more food

6. What happened to the frogs?

   A. They relocated.
   B. They were eaten.
   C. They lost their way.
   D. They found a Queen.

The Ant and the Dove

An Ant, walking by the river one day, said to himself, "How nice and cool this water looks! I must drink some of it." But as he began to drink, his foot slipped, and he fell in.

"Oh, somebody please help me, or I shall drown!" cried he.

A Dove, sitting in a tree that overhung the river, heard him, and threw him a leaf. "Climb up on that leaf," said she, "and you will float ashore."

The Ant climbed up onto the leaf, which the wind blew to the shore, and he stepped upon dry land again.

"Good-by, kind Dove," said he, as he ran home. "You have saved my life, and I wish I could do something for you."

"Good-by," said the Dove; "be careful not to fall in again."

A few days after this, when the Dove was busy building her nest, the Ant saw a man just raising his gun to shoot her.

He ran quickly, and bit the man's leg so hard that he cried "Oh! oh!" and dropped his gun.

This startled the Dove, and she flew away. The man picked up his gun, and walked on.

When he was gone, the Dove came back to her nest.

"Thank you, my little friend," she said. "You have saved my life."

And the little Ant was overjoyed to think he had been able to do for the Dove what the Dove had so lately done for him.

The author incorporates the character trait of kindness in this story. In what way is kindness shown?

Exercises

1. What does the Ant want?

   A. food
   B. a leaf
   C. a drink
   D. a family

CCSS.ELA-LITERACY.RL.3.1

4. Which word describes the Ant?

   A. grateful
   B. selfish
   C. tired
   D. lonely

CCSS.ELA-LITERACY.RL.3.4

2. What happened to the Ant?

   A. He fell into the water.
   B. He was attacked by the Dove.
   C. He lost his way.
   D. He fell asleep.

CCSS.ELA-LITERACY.RL.3.1

5. What did the Ant do?

   A. Ran away
   B. Bit the man's leg
   C. Laughed at the Dove
   D. Fell back in the water

CCSS.ELA-LITERACY.RL.3.1

3. What helps the Ant?

   A. a leaf
   B. a berry bush
   C. a lily pad
   D. a rock

CCSS.ELA-LITERACY.RL.3.1

6. Which lesson can be learned from this story?

   A. Patience pays off.
   B. Tell the truth.
   C. Help others as they have done for you.
   D. Honesty is the best policy.

CCSS.ELA-LITERACY.RL.3.2

Find detailed video explanations to each problem on:
ArgoPrep.com or Download our app: **ArgoPrep Video Explanations**

The Ox and the Frog

An Ox, drinking at a pool, chanced to set his foot on a young Frog, and crushed him to death.

His brothers and sisters, who were playing near, ran at once to tell their mother what had happened. "Oh, Mother," they cried, "a very huge beast, with four great feet, came to the pool, and crushed our brother to death in an instant, with his hard, cloven heel."

The old Frog was very vain. She was rather large, as Frogs go, and gave herself airs on account of it. "Was the cruel beast so very large?" she said. "How big?"

"Oh!" said the young Frogs. "It was a terrible monster!"

"Was it as big as this?" she said, blowing and puffing herself out.

"Oh, much bigger," replied the young Frogs.

"As big as this, then?" she added, puffing and blowing with all her might.

"A great deal bigger," they answered.

"Well, was it *so* big?"

"Oh, Mother!" cried the Frogs; "pray do not try to be so big. If you were to puff till you burst, you could not make yourself half so big as the creature we tell you of."

But the silly old Frog would not give up. She tried again to puff herself out, saying, "As big as" — and she did indeed burst.

It is useless to attempt what is impossible.

Stories contain at least one conflict, or problem. What is the problem in this story?

Exercises

1. What happened to the frog?

   A. He was left behind.
   B. He was crushed by the Ox.
   C. He was eaten by the Ox.
   D. He fell into a well.

   CCSS.ELA-LITERACY.RL.3.1

2. Which word describes the beast in the story?

   A. timid
   B. large
   C. clumsy
   D. old

   CCSS.ELA-LITERACY.RL.3.4

3. What does the mother try to do?

   A. Find the frog
   B. Find the beast
   C. Make herself as big as the beast
   D. Make herself invisible to the beast

   CCSS.ELA-LITERACY.RL.3.3

4. Which word describes the mother?

   A. foolish
   B. scared
   C. happy
   D. brave

   CCSS.ELA-LITERACY.RL.3.4

5. What happens to the mother at the end of the story?

   CCSS.ELA-LITERACY.RL.3.3

6. What lesson can you take away from this story?

   CCSS.ELA-LITERACY.RL.3.2

WEEK 16

VIDEO
EXPLANATIONS

Literal and Figurative Language

CCSS.ELA-LITERACY.L3.5.A

Literal language means exactly what it says.

Figurative language creates an image or suggests an idea that is not meant to be taken literally.

Look at these examples:

Literal: December is a winter month.

Figurative: December's icy fingertips froze everything they touched.

Literal: It is very hot outside.

Figurative: The sun's rays melted my skin as I wiped gallons of sweat from my brow.

Figurative language enhances writing and makes it more interesting to the reader.

Let's practice!

Think about your writing. Have you ever used figurative language in your stories and essays?

Exercises

Read the following sentences. Write literal or figurative on the line.

1. Thanksgiving occurs on the fourth Thursday in November.

CCSS.ELA-LITERACY.L.3.5.A

4. The teacher was smart and friendly.

CCSS.ELA-LITERACY.L.3.5.A

2. He was like a gazelle running on the track.

CCSS.ELA-LITERACY.L.3.5.A

5. After a long day at work, he slept like a log.

CCSS.ELA-LITERACY.L.3.5.A

3. The cereal crackled and popped in the milk.

CCSS.ELA-LITERACY.L.3.5.A

6. The doctor helped the patient to feel better.

CCSS.ELA-LITERACY.L.3.5.A

Week 16 - Wednesday

Find detailed video explanations to each problem on:
ArgoPrep.com or Download our app: **ArgoPrep Video Explanations**

Figurative Language – Similes and Metaphors

CCSS.ELA-LITERACY.L3.5.A

Similes and metaphors are both types of figurative language.

Similes compare two things using either "like" or "as."

Metaphors compare two things without the use of "like" or "as."

Here are some examples:

Similes:

She was as happy as a clam when she won the prize.

He was like an eager beaver as he waited in line for dessert.

Metaphor:

The teacher was a wise owl.

She was a dolphin gliding through the clear water.

Similes and metaphors are types of figurative language that can be used to compare.

Let's practice!

The word "simile" looks close to the word "smile." When you smile at someone, you "like" him or her. This can help you to remember the meaning of the word simile.

Exercises

Read the following sentences. Write simile or metaphor on the line.

1. The playground was a zoo.

4. He is as funny as a barrel of monkeys.

2. He is a night owl.

5. Joe is a chicken.

3. She was as brave as a lion.

6. Her hair is like strands of gold in the sun.

Figurative Language – Hyperboles and Personification

CCSS.ELA-LITERACY.L3.5.A

Hyperboles are a type of figurative language used to express desperation.

Personification assigns a human trait to an inanimate object.

Here are some examples:

Hyperboles:

It feels like my birthday will never come.

He is as tall as a skyscraper.

Personification:

That apple pie is calling my name.

The wind howled at night.

Figurative language is used to express thoughts in a creative way. Hyperboles are exaggerations and personification is used when human qualities are tied to non-human objects.

Let's practice!

Personification is simple to remember. Think about the word "person" at the beginning of the word. Personification describes qualities a "person" might use with non-living objects. This can help you to remember its meaning.

Exercises

Read the followings sentences. Write hyperbole or personification on the line.

1. My alarm clock yelled at me to get out of bed.

CCSS.ELA-LITERACY.L3.5.A

2. I was so angry that smoke came out of my ears.

CCSS.ELA-LITERACY.L3.5.A

3. Lightning danced across the sky.

CCSS.ELA-LITERACY.L3.5.A

4. I will die of embarrassment if I forget my lines on stage.

CCSS.ELA-LITERACY.L3.5.A

5. The sun smiled down at us.

CCSS.ELA-LITERACY.L3.5.A

6. My chores will take me five years to finish.

CCSS.ELA-LITERACY.L3.5.A

WEEK 17

VIDEO
EXPLANATIONS

ARGOPREP.COM

Find detailed video explanations to each problem on:
ArgoPrep.com or Download our app: **ArgoPrep Video Explanations**

The Stag at the Pool

A Stag overpowered by heat came to a spring to drink. Seeing his own shadow reflected in the water, he greatly admired the size and variety of his horns, but felt angry with himself for having such slender and weak feet.

While he was thus contemplating himself, a Lion appeared at the pool and crouched to spring upon him. The Stag immediately took to flight, and exerting his utmost speed, as long as the plain was smooth and open kept himself easily at a safe distance from the Lion.

But entering a wood he became entangled by his horns, and the Lion quickly came up to him and caught him.

When too late, he thus reproached himself: "Woe is me! How I have deceived myself! These feet which would have saved me I despised, and I gloried in these antlers which have proved my destruction."

What is most truly valuable is often underrated.

 *All stories have structure and are organized in certain ways. One of the most common ways to organize a story is in chronological order. This means that the story is told in the order in which the events occurred, from beginning to end.*

Exercises

1. What kind of animal is a Stag?

   A. a moose
   B. a buck
   C. a horse
   D. a donkey

   CCSS.ELA-LITERACY.RL.3.1

2. Where does the story take place?

   A. on a mountain
   B. by a spring
   C. near the sea
   D. on a snow bank

   CCSS.ELA-LITERACY.RL.3.3

3. What does the Stag see?

   A. fish
   B. plants
   C. his shadow
   D. ants

   CCSS.ELA-LITERACY.RL.3.1

4. What sneaks up on the Stag?

   A. a hunter
   B. a moose
   C. a lion
   D. a bear

   CCSS.ELA-LITERACY.RL.3.1

5. What happens to the Stag?

   A. He escapes.
   B. He becomes tangled.
   C. He falls asleep.
   D. He slips into the water.

   CCSS.ELA-LITERACY.RL.3.3

6. What lesson can you learn from this story?

   A. Tell the truth.
   B. Be kind to others.
   C. Be appreciative of what you have.
   D. Always try your best.

   CCSS.ELA-LITERACY.RL.3.2

Week 17 - Wednesday

Find detailed video explanations to each problem on:
ArgoPrep.com or Download our app: **ArgoPrep Video Explanations**

The Mouse, the Frog, and the Hawk

A Mouse, who had always lived on the land, and a Frog, who passed most of his time in the water, became friends.

The Mouse showed the Frog his nest and everything he could think of that was pleasant to see; and the Frog invited the Mouse to go home with him and see all the beautiful things that are under the water.

"Can you swim?" asked the Frog.

"Not much," said the Mouse.

"No matter," said the Frog; "I will tie your foot to my foot with a piece of this strong grass, and then I can pull you along nicely." The Frog laughed as he said this. He thought it would be good fun for him, but he well knew that the Mouse would not enjoy it.

When the Frog had tied the Mouse's foot to his own, they started together across the meadow. They soon came to the edge of the water, and the Frog jumped in, pulling the Mouse in with him.

"Oh, how cool and nice the water is, after the dry, hot land!" said the Frog, as he swam about. But the poor Mouse was frightened.

"Please let me go," said he, "or I shall die."

"Oh, never mind," said the unkind Frog; "you will get used to the water. I just love it."

But soon the poor Mouse was drowned, and floated up to the top of the water, while the Frog frisked about down below.

Just then a Hawk saw the Mouse, and pounced upon it.

As he flew away with it the Frog was dragged out of the water, too, for he was still tied to the Mouse.

"Stop, stop!" cried the Frog. "Let me go. It is the Mouse you want."

"Come along," said the Hawk; "I want you both. I will eat you first, for I like Frog meat even better than I do Mouse."

In a few moments the Hawk had made a good supper, and there was nothing left of either the false Frog or the foolish Mouse.

Diction refers to the words the author chooses to use in the story. Diction also affects the overall tone (or mood) a story has.

Exercises

1. How might you describe the Mouse and the Frog?

   A. They are enemies.
   B. They pay no attention to one another.
   C. They are jealous of one another.
   D. They are friends.

   CCSS.ELA-LITERACY.RL.3.1

4. What does the Mouse beg the Frog to do?

   A. Swim with him.
   B. Let him go.
   C. Go back to his home.
   D. Find food with him.

   CCSS.ELA-LITERACY.RL.3.3

2. Where does the Mouse go?

   A. to his home
   B. to the water
   C. to hide in a cave
   D. up a tree

   CCSS.ELA-LITERACY.RL.3.1

5. Which word describes the Frog in the story?

   A. selfish
   B. angry
   C. wise
   D. old

   CCSS.ELA-LITERACY.RL.3.4

3. How does the Mouse feel?

   A. excited
   B. brave
   C. tired
   D. scared

   CCSS.ELA-LITERACY.RL.3.3

6. What happens to the Frog and the Mouse?

   A. They remain friends forever.
   B. They become angry at one another.
   C. A Hawk eats them.
   D. They have a feast.

   CCSS.ELA-LITERACY.RL.3.3

Find detailed video explanations to each problem on:
ArgoPrep.com or Download our app: **ArgoPrep Video Explanations**

The Shepherd's Boy and the Wolf

A Man who had a fine flock of Sheep put them all into a field, and hired a Boy to take care of them, while he worked near by with his Men.

The Sheep went nibbling the grass all day, up and down the hills and along the brook; and all that the Boy had to do was to look out for the Wolf, and see that he did not come prowling into the field.

After a while the Boy began to wish that something would happen, it was so tiresome staying there all alone, with no one to speak to and nothing to do. He wished he could be with the Men in the next field, or that they could come and stay with him. All at once he thought to himself, "I will make them think the Wolf has come. That will be great fun."

So he called out as loudly as he could, "Help! help! The Wolf!" and all the Men came running up.

When they found it was only a joke, they laughed, and went back to their work.

On the next day the Boy tried the same trick again. As before, the Men dropped their mattocks and spades, for fear there might be danger, and ran to the help of the Boy. He only laughed at them for their pains, and this time they did not relish the joke. Still the Boy did not give it up. Again he shouted "Wolf! Wolf!" till the Men took no notice of him when he called them, no matter how loudly or how long he shouted.

After a while, the Wolf did get into the field. Then in real terror the Boy called and called: "Pray do come and help me. The Wolf is killing the sheep. The Wolf! the Wolf!" But no one gave heed to his cries. Finding only a terrified coward in care of the flock, the Wolf left few of them uninjured.

This story has many similar versions. Have you read some of them before? Can you think of a different ending to this particular tale?

Exercises

1. What does the word *flock* refer to in the story?

    A. shepherds
    B. group of sheep
    C. the boy
    D. many different animals

    CCSS.ELA-LITERACY.RL.3.4

4. Which does the Boy like to do?

    A. Sleep
    B. Joke
    C. Run
    D. Help

    CCSS.ELA-LITERACY.RL.3.1

2. Which of the following words can replace the word *brook* in the story?

    A. meadow
    B. hill
    C. waterfall
    D. stream

    CCSS.ELA-LITERACY.RL.3.4

5. Why do the Men become angry?

    _____
    _____
    _____
    _____
    _____
    _____

    CCSS.ELA-LITERACY.RL.3.3

3. Which word describes how the boy felt?

    A. angry
    B. sad
    C. bored
    D. excited

    CCSS.ELA-LITERACY.RL.3.4

6. What lesson can you learn from this story?

    _____
    _____
    _____
    _____
    _____
    _____

    CCSS.ELA-LITERACY.RL.3.2

WEEK 18

VIDEO
EXPLANATIONS

ARGOPREP.COM

Week 18 - Monday

Find detailed video explanations to each problem on:
ArgoPrep.com or Download our app: **ArgoPrep Video Explanations**

Figurative Language – Onomatopoeia and Alliteration

CCSS.ELA-LITERACY.L3.5.A

Figurative language creates an image or suggests an idea that is not meant to be taken literally.

Onomatopoeia is a word to describes or imitate a natural sound or the sound made by an object or an action.

Alliteration is the repetition of the same initial letter, sound, or group of sounds in a series of words.

Here are some examples:

Onomatopoeia:

snap

crackle

boom

bang

pop

Alliteration:

tiny Tim talks

sweet silly Sarah

old orange octopus

Figurative language appeals to our senses. Onomatopoeia adds sound words and alliteration uses repeated initial sounds.

Let's practice!

Incorporate onomatopoeia into your next story. Think about what words will appeal to the reader and help him or her to "hear" what is happening in your paragraphs.

Exercises

Read the following sentences. Complete each sentence with an example of onomatopoeia.

1. The bee _____ in the air.

2. My teeth started to _____ in the winter air.

3. The ducklings _____ near their mother.

4. I heard the book _____ on the desk.

Write two sentences that use alliteration in each.

5.

6.

Figurative Language – Idioms

CCSS.ELA-LITERACY.L.3.5.A

Idioms are a type of figurative language.

Idioms are expressions whose meaning is not predictable of the typical meanings of the actual words.

Here are some examples:

I had a frog in my throat.

This expression describes that concept that someone's throat is not clear, and he or she may be having trouble speaking.

I have a heart of gold.

This expression means that someone has good intentions.

I'm all ears.

This expression means that someone is listening carefully.

Idioms are another way to express ideas by using figurative language.

Let's practice!

TIP of the DAY

Idioms are useful once you understand their meanings, and are a great way to add some excitement to your writing. It is important to remember that they do not mean exactly what they say they mean.

Exercises

Read the following idioms. Write their meanings on the lines below.

1. I'm a couch potato.

CCSS.ELA-LITERACY.L.3.5.A

2. She got cold feet before the performance.

CCSS.ELA-LITERACY.L.3.5.A

3. Look on the bright side!

CCSS.ELA-LITERACY.L.3.5.A

4. I promise to zip my lips.

CCSS.ELA-LITERACY.L.3.5.A

Write two idioms below along with their meanings.

5.

CCSS.ELA-LITERACY.L.3.5.A

6.

CCSS.ELA-LITERACY.L.3.5.A

Week 18 - Friday

Find detailed video explanations to each problem on:
ArgoPrep.com or Download our app: **ArgoPrep Video Explanations**

Figurative Language – Review

CCSS.ELA-LITERACY.L3.5.A

Literal language shares exact meanings. Figurative language is used to express ideas in creative ways. There are a variety of types of figurative language that can be used to enhance your writing.

Let's review them.

Similes compare two things using either "Like" or "as."

Metaphors compare two things without the use of "like" or "as."

Hyperboles are a type of figurative language used to express desperation.

Personification assigns a human trait to an inanimate object.

Onomatopoeia is a word to describes or imitate a natural sound or the sound made by an object or an action.

Alliteration is the repetition of the same initial letter, sound, or group of sounds in a series of words.

Idioms are expressions whose meaning is not predictable of the typical meanings of the actual words.

Figurative language is used to express thoughts in a creative way.

Let's practice!

TIP of the DAY

Once you are confident with these types of figurative language, you can use them within your writing. There are several other types of figurative language too. Can you research and find another type to use as well?

Exercises

Read each example. Decide which type of figurative language is used and write it on the line.

1. I want to pick your brain.

4. She sells seashells by the seashore.

2. He is a cheetah on the football field.

5. The boiling water whistled and the tea was ready.

3. Her hair is like silk.

6. The flat tire on her brand new car laughed at her.

WEEK 19

VIDEO
EXPLANATIONS

ARGOPREP.COM

The Fisherman and the Little Fish

All day long a Fisherman had been toiling and had caught nothing.

"I will make one more effort," thought he, "and then I must go home."

He threw in his line, and soon drew up a very small perch.

The little Fish was terribly frightened when he found himself out of water, and with a sharp hook sticking in his mouth; and he said to the Fisherman:

"O sir, take pity upon me, and throw me into the water again! See what a little thing I am. I should not make one mouthful for you now; but if you leave me in the water, I shall grow large and stout, and then I shall be worth catching. You can make a dinner of me then, or sell me for a good price."

"Ah!" said the Fisherman, "it is true you are small, but I have you safely now. If I should throw you back, I might never catch you again. You are better than nothing. I will keep you"; and he put the little Fish into his basket, and took him home with him.

TIP of the **DAY**

What point of view is this story told from? Authors use various viewpoints to tell stories from different angles. Sometimes the person telling the story has an active part in it. Sometimes the person telling the story is on the outside looking in.

Exercises

1. What is wrong with the Fisherman?

    A. He has not caught any fish.
    B. He forgot his bait.
    C. His fishing line broke.
    D. His fishing rod fell into the water.

CCSS.ELA-LITERACY.RL.3.1

4. What does the perch hope the Fisherman will do?

    A. Take him home
    B. Throw him back
    C. Eat him
    D. Become friends with him

CCSS.ELA-LITERACY.RL.3.3

2. What is another word that can replace *perch* in the story?

    A. sit
    B. rest
    C. fish
    D. tadpole

CCSS.ELA-LITERACY.RL.3.4

5. Which word describes the perch?

    A. strong
    B. foolish
    C. old
    D. little

CCSS.ELA-LITERACY.RL.3.4

3. What does it mean to take pity on someone?

    A. Be unkind to them
    B. Feel sorry for them
    C. Tell a lie about them
    D. Listen to them

CCSS.ELA-LITERACY.RL.3.4

6. What happens to the perch?

    A. The fisherman takes him home.
    B. The fisherman throws him back in the water.
    C. The fisherman shares him with his wife.
    D. The fisherman drops him and he gets away.

CCSS.ELA-LITERACY.RL.3.3

The Fox and the Crow

A Crow stole a piece of cheese one day, and flew with it up into a tree, so as to eat it at her leisure.

As she sat there, holding it in her beak, a Fox chanced to pass by, and looking up saw her. "How good that cheese smells!" thought he; "I'll have it, sure as I'm a Fox."

Coming close to the tree, he said, "My dear Madam, what a beautiful creature you are! I was not aware till this moment what rare beauty your family possesses. What eyes! What glossy feathers! What grace of form! Is your voice as charming to hear, as your person is to look upon? If it is, you well deserve to be called the Queen of Birds. Will you not do me the favor to sing to me?"

Now it is well known that the Caw! Caw! of the Crow family is not musical. She ought to have been on her guard, but so delighted was she with the flattery of the Fox that she forgot to be wary. She opened her mouth to show the Fox the sweetness of her voice, when — down fell the bit of cheese, which was exactly what was expected.

The Fox ate it at one mouthful, then stopped to say, "Thank you, madam. I am quite satisfied. Your voice is well enough, I have no doubt. What a pity it is you are so sadly wanting in wit!"

The Crow learned that we do well to be on our guard when people flatter us.

What elements of this story show the reader that it is not a true tale? Think about the characters and their actions. What clues do they give the reader about the story's genre?

Exercises

1. What does the Crow do?

   A. Steals a piece of cheese
   B. Takes a nest
   C. Flies into a window
   D. Argues with a pigeon

   CCSS.ELA-LITERACY.RL.3.1

4. What does the Fox ask the Crow to do?

   A. share lunch
   B. travel with him
   C. sing to him
   D. tell him a story

   CCSS.ELA-LITERACY.RL.3.1

2. Which word describes the Fox?

   A. foolish
   B. sly
   C. kind
   D. excited

   CCSS.ELA-LITERACY.RL.3.4

5. What does the word *flattery* mean in the story?

   A. music
   B. lies
   C. praise
   D. story

   CCSS.ELA-LITERACY.RL.3.4

3. Which word can replace *charming* in the story?

   A. rude
   B. eager
   C. pleasant
   D. happy

   CCSS.ELA-LITERACY.RL.3.4

6. What does the Fox get from the Crow?

   A. music lessons
   B. a new friendship
   C. a home
   D. food

   CCSS.ELA-LITERACY.RL.3.1

Find detailed video explanations to each problem on:
ArgoPrep.com or Download our app: **ArgoPrep Video Explanations**

The Hares and the Frogs

In a forest, deep, shady, and still, there once lived a company of Hares.

Whenever a leaf fell rustling to the ground, or a squirrel, jumping in the branches, broke a twig, the Hares started and trembled, they were so timid.

One day there came a great wind, rushing through the tops of the trees with a roaring noise, and waving the branches back and forth.

It frightened the Hares so much that they all started together, running as fast as they could to get out of the forest, which had been their home.

"What a sad state is ours," they said, "never to eat in comfort, to sleep always in fear, to be startled by a shadow, and fly with beating heart at the rustling of the leaves. Better death, by far. Let us drown ourselves in yonder lake."

But when they came to the lake, it happened that there were scores of frogs sporting on the banks; who, when they heard the sound of footsteps, jumped into the water.

The timid Hares were startled by the splash; but, as they saw the frogs dive to the bottom of the lake, a wise old Hare said, "Stop a moment! Let us consider. Here are creatures that are more timid than we — they are afraid even of us. See, they are drowning themselves for fear of us! It may not be so bad with us as we thought. Perhaps we have been foolish, as foolish as the frogs, who are alarmed when there is no danger. Let us make the best of our lot, and try to be brave in it." So back they went again to the forest.

The author uses a descriptive style for this piece of writing. The reader learns details about the way the forest looks, its sounds, and the characters. Descriptive writing allows you to picture a story as you read.

Exercises

1. Which word describes the Hares?

    A. shy
    B. tall
    C. naughty
    D. old

CCSS.ELA-LITERACY.RL.3.4

4. What do the Hares think about the Frogs?

    A. They are kind.
    B. They are foolish.
    C. They are brave.
    D. They must be lost.

CCSS.ELA-LITERACY.RL.3.3

2. What bothers the Hares?

    A. the other animals
    B. the rain
    C. the hot sun
    D. the noisy trees

CCSS.ELA-LITERACY.RL.3.1

5. What do the Hares decide they should do?

CCSS.ELA-LITERACY.RL.3.1

3. What is the setting of the story?

    A. in a rabbit hole
    B. in a cave
    C. near a brook
    D. deep in the forest

CCSS.ELA-LITERACY.RL.3.1

6. What does the wise Hare share with the other Hares?

CCSS.ELA-LITERACY.RL.3.2

WEEK 20

VIDEO
EXPLANATIONS

ARGOPREP.COM

Spelling Patterns – Inflectional Endings (double consonants)

CCSS.ELA-LITERACY.L.3.2.F

Many words follow certain patterns. Knowing and understanding these patterns can help you to become a strong reader and writer.

When adding a word ending such as –ed or –ing, the consonant is often doubled at the end of the original word. This ensures that the short vowel sound of the base word is still maintained.

Here are some examples:

stop + ing = stopping

Notice that the letter p at the end of stop is now doubled.

sit + ing = sitting

Again, the t at the end of the word is doubled to form the new word.

hug + ed = hugged

The g is doubled to form the word hugged.

Double the final consonant in words that contain a single vowel. Then add a new ending to form a new word.

Let's practice!

Many common words follow the double consonant -ed rule. Can you think of more examples that fit this spelling pattern?

Exercises

Read the following. Spell the new word on the line.

1. swim + ing = _____

CCSS.ELA-LITERACY.L.3.2.F

4. refer + ed = _____

CCSS.ELA-LITERACY.L.3.2.F

2. stir + ed = _____

CCSS.ELA-LITERACY.L.3.2.F

5. run + ing = _____

CCSS.ELA-LITERACY.L.3.2.F

3. drip + ing = _____

CCSS.ELA-LITERACY.L.3.2.F

6. prefer + ed = _____

CCSS.ELA-LITERACY.L.3.2.F

Week 20 - Wednesday

Find detailed video explanations to each problem on:
ArgoPrep.com or Download our app: **ArgoPrep Video Explanations**

Spelling Patterns – Inflectional Endings (y to i)

CCSS.ELA-LITERACY.L.3.2.F

Many words follow certain patterns. Knowing and understanding these patterns can help you to become a strong reader and writer.

When a word ends with the letter –y, change the –y to an –i before adding the –ed ending.

Here are some examples:

carry + ed = carried

Notice that the letter y has been dropped and an I has replaced it.

try + ed = tried

Again, the y at the end of the word is dropped and replaced with an i to form the new word.

bury + ed = buried

The y is removed and replaced with an i to form the word buried.

Drop the –y and replace it with an –i. Then add the –ed ending to form a new word.

Let's practice!

This same rule also applies when using the -es ending. For example, the word "carry" can become the word "carries."

I carry the yellow balloons.
She carries the red balloons.

Exercises

Read the following. Spell the new word on the line.

1. dry + ed = _____

CCSS.ELA-LITERACY.L.3.2.F

4. copy + ed = _____

CCSS.ELA-LITERACY.L.3.2.F

2. rely + ed = _____

CCSS.ELA-LITERACY.L.3.2.F

5. hurry + ed = _____

CCSS.ELA-LITERACY.L.3.2.F

3. steady + ed = _____

CCSS.ELA-LITERACY.L.3.2.F

6. study + ed = _____

CCSS.ELA-LITERACY.L.3.2.F

Find detailed video explanations to each problem on:
ArgoPrep.com or Download our app: **ArgoPrep Video Explanations**

Spelling Patterns – Complex Consonants (-tch and -ch)

CCSS.ELA-LITERACY.L.3.2.F

Many words contain consonant clusters, when two or more consonants work together to make a sound, like –tch and –ch.

When a short vowel is heard before a /ch/ sound in a word that is one syllable, the word will most likely be spelled with the –tch. The t is silent.

> catch, fetch

When a short vowel sound is followed with a consonant sound in a one-syllable word, the final /ch/ sound is spelled ch.

> rich, munch

Understanding these rules can help you to become a strong writer.

Let's practice!

Identifying spelling patterns and remembering them can help you to become a better reader. The next time you read a book for enjoyment, pick a few spelling patterns to focus on. Keep a piece of paper with your book, and write down as many words as you find that fit each pattern. Challenge yourself to guess which pattern will have the most, and then see if you were correct.

Exercises

Read the following. Sort the words into the correct column. Then add one additional word in each column at the end.

bench	scratch	itch	arch	munch

catch	torch	hunch	touch	patch

-tch	-ch

CCSS.ELA-LITERACY.L.3.2.F

CCSS.ELA-LITERACY.L.3.2.F

ANSWER KEYS

VIDEO EXPLANATIONS

ARGOPREP.COM

Answer Keys

Find detailed video explanations to each problem on:
ArgoPrep.com or Download our app: **ArgoPrep Video Explanations**

Week 1

Monday
1. A
2. D
3. A
4. C
5. B
6. B

Wednesday
1. B
2. A
3. B
4. A
5. B
6. C

Friday
1. D
2. C
3. C
4. A
5. Neville watches the sun and the clouds in the sky.
6. Answers will vary and should describe something that might happen to Neville after he begins talking with the horse.

Week 2

Monday
1. plural
2. singular
3. singular
Answers will vary, but should include a response that fits in the sentence.
4. (a plural noun) possible answer: brothers
5. (a singular noun) possible answer: kitten
6. (a singular noun) possible answer: light bulb

Wednesday
1. benches
2. butterflies
3. potatoes
4. families
5. elves
6. wishes

Friday
1. sheep
2. people
3. oxen
4. men
5. fish
6. cacti

Week 3

Monday
1. C
2. B
3. B
4. C
5. D
6. A

Wednesday
1. C
2. B
3. D
4. B
5. B
6. C

Friday
1. B
2. B
3. A
4. C
5. Answers may vary, but should share that Teenty-Tawnty goes into the woods and is looking for fish in the water.
6. Answers may vary, but should make a prediction about what might happen to Teenty-Tawnty after she begins talking to the fish.

Week 4

Monday
1. sight, sound
2. sight, sound, feel
3. sight, sound, taste, taste, hear
4. sight, feel
5. sight, feel, taste, smell
6. sight, hear

Wednesday
1. joy
2. kindness
3. pride
4. loyalty
5. brilliance
6. bravery

Friday
1. anger, baseball, Dad's
2. love, children
3. grandpa, wisdom
4. humor, students, Teacher's
5. Joe, luck, game
6. honesty, police officer

Week 5

Monday
1. B
2. C
3. A
4. A
5. C
6. C

Wednesday
1. B
2. D
3. A
4. B
5. D
6. A

 Find detailed video explanations to each problem on:
ArgoPrep.com or Download our app: **ArgoPrep Video Explanations**

Friday
1. A
2. C
3. B
4. C
5. He takes her on his horse and leaves.
6. Answers will vary but should include a response about what might happen next to the maiden after the prince took her away on his horse.

Week 6

·Monday
1. play
2. worries
3. puts
4. looks
5. orders
6. need

Wednesday
Answers will vary, but should end in –ed as a past tense verb. Possible answers are listed here.
1. closed
2. picked
3. walked
4. played
5. talked
6. rested

Friday
Answers will vary, but should include *will* as part of a present tense verb. Possible answers are listed here.
1. will play
2. will study
3. will go
4. will move
5. will fly
6. will fit

Week 7

Monday
1. B
2. B
3. A
4. A
5. A
6. D

Wednesday
1. A
2. A
3. B
4. C
5. D
6. B

Friday
1. D
2. C
3. C
4. A
5. The birds decide to determine a King by seeing which one can fly the highest in the sky.
6. Answers will vary, but should discuss which bird might become King with reasons to support the choice.

Week 8

Monday
1. She loves to read.
2. They live in Alabama.
3. They misbehaved during recess.
4. They ran under the deck.
5. She was crying before her nap.
6. She was absent from school.

Wednesday
1. our

2. his
3. his
4. her
5. her
6. their

Friday
1. their, P
2. her, S
3. their, P
4. her, S
5. I, S
6. his, S

Week 9

Monday
1. C
2. D
3. A
4. B
5. A
6. C

Wednesday
1. D
2. A
3. D
4. C
5. B
6. C

Friday
1. D
2. A
3. C
4. D
5. The author thinks October is a great month for many reasons, including the blue skies, bright leaves, fragrant grapes, etc...
6. Answers will vary, but may include fall activities like raking and jumping in the leaves, eating fall foods, fall festivals, etc...

Week 10

Monday
1. yellow
2. pretty
3. blue
4. four
5. one
6. small

Wednesday
Answers will vary. Possible answers are below.
1. quieter
2. older
3. slower
Sentences will vary but should use the given comparative adjective.
4. The sun was brighter today than yesterday.
5. She is faster than her sister.
6. That painting is lower than the other one.

Friday
Answers will vary. Possible answers are below.
1. tallest
2. fastest
3. neatest
Sentences will vary but should use the given superlative adjective.
4. She is the shortest in her dance class.
5. He is always the quietest student in the library.
6. That is the biggest gift of all the presents under the tree.

Week 11

Monday
1. C
2. B
3. A
4. B
5. D
6. A

Wednesday
1. C
2. D
3. B
4. A
5. C
6. D

Friday
1. B
2. A
3. C
4. D
5. She tells them that they need to leave.
6. You should be careful to take care of yourself first.

Week 12

Monday
1. Lila, Debbie, and Joan
2. Texas, New York, Minnesota, and Idaho
3. none
4. movies, ice skating, and shopping
5. Derek, Timothy, Rich, Joe, and Justin
6. Hannah, Elizabeth, and Mariah Rose

Wednesday
1. Lisa lives in Los Angeles, California.
2. The city of Albuquerque, New Mexico is a beautiful place to explore.
3. The diner is located at 439 Little Lane, West Newton, Ohio.
4. The foreign language students will go on a trip to Paris, France on May 23, 2020.
5. We will soon move to 9845 West Dover Street in Middleton, Delaware.
6. Georgia visited her aunt on July 18, 2019 in Raleigh, North Carolina.

Friday
1. Tony told Sammi, "I will be back by seven o'clock."
2. Delaney, Josh, and Sarah all chanted, "Go, team, go!"
3. After visiting her aunt, Myra thanked her and said, "See you soon!"
4. John told the doctor, "I have had a headache for three days now."
5. After leaving for her trip, Caroline called her mom and told her, "My flight will land at nine thirty tonight."
6. Before going to school, Jeff's mom asked him, "Did you remember to get your lunchbox?"

Week 13

Monday
1. A
2. B
3. D
4. B
5. A
6. D

Wednesday
1. D
2. C
3. B
4. A
5. A
6. C

Friday
1. A

 Answer Keys

Find detailed video explanations to each problem on:
ArgoPrep.com or Download our app: **ArgoPrep Video Explanations**

2. D
3. A
4. C
5. He notices that he shakes his ears sometimes.
6. Be careful for what you wish for and happy with yourself.

Week 14

Monday
1. and
2. or
3. yet
4. or
5. so
6. but

Wednesday
1. I had that book, but I lost it.
2. David moved to Florida, but he moved home shortly after.
3. Melissa can bake the cake, and Theresa can cook the chicken.
4. I can go to the store, and I can go to the bank.
5. They didn't want to be late to school, so they walked quickly.
6. The summer is my favorite time of the year, but the spring time is nice too.

Friday
1. It is surprising that you didn't join the chess club.
2. I can't relax until I find my puppy.
3. I am going to go inside her house since it's raining.
4. Greg felt proud when he earned a good grade.
5. The teacher read the rules before she started her lesson.
6. Erin couldn't go to school because she was sick.

Week 15

Monday
1. C
2. B
3. C
4. C
5. A
6. B

Wednesday
1. C
2. A
3. A
4. A
5. B
6. C

Friday
1. B
2. B
3. C
4. A
5. She tries to become as big as the beast by puffing her cheeks up, and she bursts.
6. Do not attempt things that are not possible.

Week 16

Monday
1. literal
2. figurative
3. figurative
4. literal
5. figurative
6. literal

Wednesday
1. metaphor
2. metaphor
3. simile
4. simile
5. metaphor
6. simile

Friday
1. personification
2. hyperbole
3. personification
4. hyperbole
5. personification
6. hyperbole

Week 17

Monday
1. B
2. B
3. C
4. C
5. B
6. C

Wednesday
1. D
2. B
3. D
4. B
5. A
6. C

Friday
1. B
2. D
3. C
4. B
5. The boy calls for help over and over, but he is joking and does not truly need help.
6. Tell the truth or others will no longer believe you.

Week 18

Monday
1. buzzed
2. chattered
3. quacked
4. slam
5. and 6. Answers will vary but should include examples of alliteration.

Wednesday

1. I'm lazy.
2. She was nervous.
3. Focus on the positive.
4. I promise not to tell.
5. and 6. Answers will vary, but should include an idiom and its explanation.

Friday

1. idiom
2. metaphor
3. simile
4. alliteration
5. onomatopoeia
6. personification

Week 19

Monday

1. A
2. C
3. B
4. B
5. D
6. A

Wednesday

1. A
2. B
3. C
4. C
5. C
6. D

Friday

1. A
2. D
3. D
4. B
5. They decide to drown themselves because they cannot be happy.
6. The wise Hare tells them to be brave and make the best of their lives.

Week 20

Monday

1. Swimming = _____
2. Stirred = _____
3. Dripping = _____
4. Referred = _____
5. Running = _____
6. Preferred = _____

Wednesday

1. dried
2. relied
3. steadied
4. copied
5. hurried
6. studied

Friday

-tch	-ch
scratch	bench
itch	arch
catch	munch
patch	torch
	hunch
	touch

*Students should add one additional word in each column as well.

Reference

The Project Gutenberg EBook of My Father's Dragon, by Ruth Stiles Gannett
http://www.gutenberg.org/cache/epub/30017/pg30017.txt

Week 1, Monday

Project Gutenberg's A Book for Kids, by C. J. (Clarence Michael James) Dennis
http://www.gutenberg.org/cache/epub/19993/pg19993.txt

Week 1, Wednesday

Project Gutenberg's A Book for Kids, by C. J. (Clarence Michael James) Dennis
http://www.gutenberg.org/cache/epub/19993/pg19993.txt

Week 1, Friday

The Project Gutenberg EBook of The Conceited Pig, by Anonymous
http://www.gutenberg.org/files/59983/59983-0.txt

Week 3, Monday

The Project Gutenberg EBook of Poems Teachers Ask For, by Various
http://www.gutenberg.org/cache/epub/18909/pg18909.txt

Week 3, Wednesday

The Project Gutenberg EBook of Stories of Childhood, by Various
http://www.gutenberg.org/cache/epub/15933/pg15933.txt

Week 3, Friday

The Project Gutenberg EBook of The Blue Fairy Book, by Various
http://www.gutenberg.org/files/503/503-0.txt

Week 5, Monday

The Project Gutenberg EBook of The Blue Fairy Book, by Various
http://www.gutenberg.org/files/503/503-0.txt

Week 5, Wednesday

The Project Gutenberg EBook of The Blue Fairy Book, by Various
http://www.gutenberg.org/files/503/503-0.txt

Week 5, Friday

The Project Gutenberg EBook of Grimm's Fairy Tales, by Various
http://www.gutenberg.org/files/52521/52521-0.txt

Week 7, Monday

The Project Gutenberg EBook of Grimm's Fairy Tales, by Various
http://www.gutenberg.org/files/52521/52521-0.txt

Week 7, Wednesday

The Project Gutenberg EBook of Grimm's Fairy Tales, by Various
http://www.gutenberg.org/files/52521/52521-0.txt

Week 7, Friday

Project Gutenberg's More Bed-Time Stories, by Louise Chandler Moulton
http://www.gutenberg.org/cache/epub/60581/pg60581.txt

Week 9, Monday

Project Gutenberg's More Bed-Time Stories, by Louise Chandler Moulton
http://www.gutenberg.org/cache/epub/60581/pg60581.txt

Week 9, Wednesday

The Project Gutenberg EBook of Poems Teachers Ask For, by Various
http://www.gutenberg.org/cache/epub/18909/pg18909.txt

Week 9, Friday